CONTENTS

SECTION A – CONTEXT

SECTION B – TECHNOLOGY

SECTION C – FINANCE

SECTION D – PRACTICALITIES

SECTION E – RENEWABLE ELECTRICITY UPDATE

Appendices

SUMMARY OF KEY ISSUES

- The Renewable Heat Incentive could make the economics of investing in a renewable heating system more attractive to property owners and occupiers.

- Control over the heat source, be that solar, own grown biomass, or ground heat, gives more security to the owner than relying on purchased feedstock.

- A review of the energy efficiency of the buildings is a sensible starting point, so that any improvements can be considered as part of an integrated package.

- Where projects depend on the RHI for viability, care should be taken to ensure that the necessary tariff rate can be secured, with contingency plans in place should changes to the rates be proposed – as happened with Feed-in Tariffs for solar power.

PROJECT APPRAISAL CHECK LIST

As with any new project involving substantial expenditure (and often borrowing), property owners and lenders looking at renewable heat should properly evaluate the issues and risks they are taking on. How vulnerable are the economics of the project to cost and time over-runs, technical failures, shortcomings in efficiencies, changing markets, questions over the supply of parts or feedstock, regulatory issues and the many other factors, often unforeseen, which can affect the viability of both installation and operation? Careful assessment of the risks and sensitivity analysis allowing for such factors is important – especially to demonstrate the project's viability to a lender.

Also of fundamental importance is the fact that such a project is not just an investment, but will also be the source of heat on which the owner and tenants may be reliant for domestic comfort and commercial success.

This check list highlights some of the key factors which property owners and their advisers may wish to consider before embarking on a renewable heat project. The list cannot be exhaustive but may be useful as a starting point, both for renewable heat schemes and on a more general basis, other renewable energy projects.

Risks with the equipment/ technology:
– Is the technology well established or innovative?
– Can it be seen operating elsewhere in the UK?
– Are the claims made for its performance verifiable?
– Creditworthiness of suppliers
– Availability and cost of spares and servicing – in the area, in the UK or from abroad? Now and in the future?
– How up to date is the technology / system?

Risks with the project team:
– Competence of designers, contractors and project managers: their experience and track record
– Contract terms
– Insurance
– Could they stand making good a major failure in the project during installation?
– Health and safety issues relating to overseas contractors (e.g. German contractors may be unused to CDM Regulations as these are understood not to apply in Germany, with potential difficulties on a UK site).

Planning consent:
– Time and cost to obtain
– Terms and conditions – temporary or permanent?
– Conditions on sourcing feedstock, working hours, vehicle movements etc

Landlord – tenant issues:
– Landlord supplying heat:
  • Terms of heat supply agreement
  • Charges and reviews
  • Contingency plans and back-up systems
– Tenant installing plant:
  • Landlord's consent for tenant's improvements
  • End of tenancy issues

Feedstock:
– Source, reliability, cost
– Storage – suitability and of a size sufficient to cover problems over supply?
– Contingencies if supply fails or becomes too dear – back-up systems
– Energy crops – risk of future regulation? Opportunity cost against other crops?

Operational Issues:
– Are there the skills and time available to manage the operation of the equipment?
– What is the fallback means for providing heat if the scheme is inadequate, out for servicing or fails?
– Arrangements for maintenance – will the installer offer a maintenance contract?

Finance:
– Business plan – has this been sensitivity checked for delays, over-runs and problems?
– Is a loan needed? Business case, application, security, servicing.
– Valuations of security – for project? Does the project alter the value of other property already secured or usable as security?
– Does the scheme qualify for RHI payments? Other payments?
– Are other grants available? If so, will they prevent the project being eligible for RHI?
– Can heat be sold?
– Other income streams?
– Liabilities to customers?

Contingency plans:
– Cost overrun
– With the prospect of strong demand in coming months for installations, can manufacturers, suppliers and installers keep pace properly?
– Construction delays
– Delays in Ofgem accreditation
– Delays in commissioning – risk to RHI tariff rates

SECTION A: CONTEXT

1. INTRODUCTION

1.1   The use of buildings makes heavy demands on energy resources, whether it be for heating (or cooling) the internal environment; for heat used in commercial and industrial processes; or for heating water to clean people, equipment or the fabric of the building itself. The preamble to EU Directive 2010/31/EU on the Energy Performance of Buildings estimates that "buildings account for 40% of total energy consumption in the Union". In an era where policies aim to reduce energy consumption and switch it to more sustainable sources, the heating of buildings is an obvious target.

1.2   The very nature of buildings presents both problems and solutions to policy makers. On the one hand, they are relatively easy to identify and they do not move – this makes them easier to measure, inspect and tax than some other energy users. On the other hand, the very great majority of existing buildings (perhaps especially those built in the twentieth century) were designed and built with little thought for the energy which would be consumed within them, or how this might be minimised through good design and construction techniques, meaning that there is a great deal to do to catch up. Modern expectations for central heating and, increasingly, air conditioning, mean that much more energy is being used in buildings than ever before. New 'low carbon' design and building standards can improve the buildings of the future, but the structures we are using today and which we will be continuing to use for many years to come, present a greater technical and policy challenge.

1.3   In this context the UK Government has now introduced the Renewable Heat Incentive (RHI) to encourage the owners and occupiers of buildings to switch to qualifying renewable heat sources. The RHI will provide a continuous income stream for twenty years to anyone who installs and uses an eligible renewable heating system, reducing the cost barrier and making it more financially attractive than a fossil fuel alternative. As it is anticipated that capital costs of equipment will fall with increased demand and wider uptake, so the size of payments made through the RHI is expected to decrease in future years – a policy known as degressivity.

1.4   The initial proposals apply to non-domestic property (which in this context means anything other than a single dwelling), but a further package of measures aimed at domestic property is expected later in 2012.

1.5   Renewable heat is likely to be of particular interest where buildings are located off the mains gas grid, as in many rural areas. Rural properties are more likely to be dependent on relatively expensive oil or calor gas and hence heating forms a higher proportion of their running costs. Conversely, such properties will more frequently have characteristics which make them particularly suitable for renewable heating systems, such as access to wood, straw or other biomass fuels; or having a sufficient land area to support a ground source heat pump. When a source of funds is available to offset the additional capital cost of renewable technology, the prospect of a free (solar or ground source) or in-hand (biomass) source of energy can be a most attractive one, particularly in today's volatile global commodity markets.

1.6   Aside from any direct financial gain, some may see that investing in low emissions systems will be of benefit to their business in other ways, from meeting tighter environmental standards for supermarket contracts to being able to promote conference venues or holiday accommodation as 'environmentally friendly'. Some will see this as a way to reduce the 'embodied carbon' in their products, while larger businesses with corporate social responsibility obligations may find that the installation of renewable heating systems helps them to meet some of those obligations.

1.7   Much of the technology discussed in this paper is still relatively new in the United Kingdom and Valuers should take care to ensure that they have made thorough enquiries before advising clients. Some further sources of information are listed in Appendix II and a Glossary of Terms is included at Appendix III.

2. POLICY BACKGROUND

2.1 Introduction

2.1.1 A detailed review of UK and EU energy policy is included in Appendix B of CAAV Numbered Publication 203: The On-Farm Generation of Renewable Electricity.

2.1.2 The main framework for UK energy policy is set at the European level, within the larger structure of international agreements such as the Kyoto Accord. National governments then develop means to implement EU Directives and deliver their targets. Energy policy remains largely administered at UK level by the Department of Energy and Climate Change (DECC), but there is some executive devolution to Scotland and the policy issues touch on many other areas of devolved policy, such as development control. Energy generation is fully devolved in Northern Ireland.

2.2 European Policy

2.2.1 Much of the policy direction for renewable energy is driven by carbon reduction targets agreed at the EU level.

2.2.2 The Renewable Energy Directive 2009/28/EC was published in June 2009 and set a target of 20% of all energy consumed in the EU to be from renewable sources by 2020. Different member states have their own targets to feed into that overall figure; the target for the UK is 15%, recognising that we lag behind much of Europe due in part to our dependence on North Sea oil and gas in recent decades. The Directive also required that all member states produce a renewables action plan (see paragraph 2.5.2 for commentary on the UK plan).

2.2.3 More recently, the EU Commission's Communication "A roadmap for moving to a competitive low carbon economy in 2050", published in March 2011, confirms the aim of reducing domestic greenhouse gas emissions in the EU by 80% (compared to 1990 levels) by 2050. It identifies the built environment as an important sector, capable of reducing emissions by 90% by 2050. It proposes that the use of renewable energy to heat buildings is part of the solution, along with improved building standards and financial incentives to support energy efficiency measures in existing buildings.

2.3 The Energy Performance of Buildings Directive

2.3.1 EU Directive 2010/31/EU on the Energy Performance of Buildings was issued on 19th May 2010, recasting the 2002 Directive. Member states must enact legislation to implement the Directive by 9th July 2012 with most provisions to take effect from 9th January 2013. Some of the requirements of the Directive are already met by existing UK legislation, but others will require new regulations.

2.3.2 The Directive sets a framework for requiring member states to set and enforce minimum standards to be applied to the energy performance of:
- new buildings
- existing buildings subject to 'major renovation'
- technical systems on installation or when upgraded.

2.3.3 The Directive also requires that member states
- have national plans for increasing the number of "nearly zero-energy" buildings
- require energy performance certification of buildings on construction, sale or lease

- require regular inspection of larger heating and air-conditioning systems
- establish independent regulation of systems for energy performance certificates and inspections.

2.3.4   Member states may set higher standards than the Directive and while the Coalition Government has generally pledged not to "gold-plate" regulations unnecessarily, this area is recognised as an important one which may mean that higher standards could be sought.

2.3.5   The Directive requires member states to establish and apply a methodology for calculating the energy performance of buildings within its common framework. That methodology will take account not only of the thermal characteristics of the building itself, with its integral systems, but also "active solar systems and other heating and electricity systems based on energy from renewable sources" (Annex 1, para 4(a)). There is an underlying emphasis on the use of energy from alternative and renewable sources.

2.3.6   Member states are to set minimum energy performance standards for buildings to achieve "cost-optimal levels". These standards may distinguish between new and existing buildings and between different categories of buildings. Those standards are to be enforced for new buildings and where existing buildings are subject to "major renovation" (see paragraph 2.4.4 below). It may be that more generally they will lead to increased building standards.

2.3.7   The Directive also records a policy expectation for member states that, by 2020, new buildings should be "nearly zero-energy".

2.4   Energy Performance Certificates

2.4.1   The Directive carries forward the system of Energy Performance Certificates (EPCs) created by the 2002 Directive assessing and recording the energy rating of most buildings with recommendations for improvements to their energy efficiency. Subject to certain possible exceptions, buildings are required to have an EPC if they are to be sold, to let, and on construction if:
- they are structures with walls and a roof
- they use energy to condition the indoor climate.

2.4.2   Article 4 of the European Directive allows member states the discretion to say that EPCs are not required for the following types of building:
   (a) buildings officially protected as part of a designated environment or because of their special architectural or historical merit, in so far as compliance with certain minimum energy performance requirements would unacceptably alter their character or appearance;
   (b) buildings used as places of worship and for religious activities;
   (c) temporary buildings with a time of use of two years or less, industrial sites, workshops and non-residential agricultural buildings with low energy demand and non-residential agricultural buildings which are in use by a sector covered by a national sectoral agreement on energy performance;
   (d) residential buildings which are used or intended to be used for either less than four months of the year or, alternatively, for a limited annual time of use and with an expected energy consumption of less than 25% of what would be the result of all-year use;
   (e) stand-alone buildings with a total useful floor area of less than 50m^2.

2.4.3   The UK has implemented the Directive by the Energy Performance of Buildings (Certificates and Inspections) (England and Wales) Regulations 2007 SI 991 (as amended) and the Energy Performance of Buildings (Scotland) Regulations 2008 SSI 309 (as amended). In England and Wales an EPC is not required for:
- buildings used as places of worship and for religious activities;
- temporary buildings with a time of use of two years or less, industrial sites, workshops and non-residential agricultural buildings with low energy demand;
- stand-alone buildings with a total useful floor area of less than $50m^2$.

In Scotland only the following categories are exempt:
- temporary buildings with a planned time of use of two years or less, workshops and non-residential agricultural buildings with low energy demand;
- stand-alone buildings with a total useful floor area of less than $50m^2$ which are not dwellings.

2.4.4   **Major renovations** – Where a building has a 'major renovation', the Directive now requires the member state to choose whether either the whole building or the renovated part is to meet current minimum energy performance requirements. 'Major renovation' is defined in two different ways in the Directive and it is for each member state to decide which interpretation they will choose. The alternatives are considered in more detail in Appendix IV.

2.4.5   If the renovation proves to be "major" under the test adopted by the member state, then the Directive appears to let the member state's legislation say whether it is the whole building or just the renovated part of it that is to be ungraded to minimum energy performance standards.

2.5   United Kingdom Policy
2.5.1   The Department of Communities and Local Government estimates that 42% of all carbon emissions in the UK come from buildings, with about 20% coming from non-residential property. The 2007 Energy White Paper 'Meeting the Energy Challenge' committed the Government to develop policy options which would reduce the carbon impact of heat. The approach to date has been to focus on the de-carbonisation of the electricity supply (by increasing generation from wind and other renewable sources) so that electrical sources can be used for heat and transport energy. With the increasing electricity demand that that goal implies in a country with a growing population, that is an enormous challenge.

2.5.2   In July 2010 the Government submitted the UK Renewable Energy Action Plan to the European Commission. It estimated that the share of UK heat demand met from renewable sources needs to increase from 1% today to around 12% in 2020 to help meet the overall 2020 target of 15% of all UK energy needs being met from renewable sources. The latest figures produced by the Department of Energy and Climate Change state that heat produced from renewable sources increased by 17% between 2009 and 2010 to 1,212 ktoe (kilo tonnes of oil equivalent) (Digest of UK Energy Statistics 2011).

2.5.3   The Renewable Energy Action Plan required further work to consider how the barriers to the uptake of renewable heat in the domestic sector could be overcome, leading to the development of the strategy 'Warm Homes, Greener Homes: A Strategy for Household Energy Management', which was published in 2010. This concentrates on improving the efficiency of energy used for heat in the home in order to meet a target of a 29% reduction of carbon emissions from the household sector. The strategy proposes:
- By 2015 every household to have installed loft and cavity wall insulation where it is practical to do so;

- By 2020 up to 7 million homes to have received eco-upgrades, including improvements such as solid wall insulation or renewable energy generating technologies;
- A 'Pay As You Save' system to remove the deterrent of upfront costs and reduce the difficulty of the move to greener living.

The Government is now considering how it might deliver these aspirations.

2.5.4   Some of these elements will be brought together in the 'Green Deal' – a policy to support the reduction of carbon emissions in domestic property which is expected to be launched in 2012 (see paragraph 11.0). It is a major part of the Coalition Government's energy policy, but the information announced so far lacks detail. However, it is expected that the scheme will include energy audits of property to identify potential savings and the opportunity for cost-effective investments. It will then allow the initial costs of capital works designed to reduce emissions to be repaid from future energy bills, by linking the payment for the works to the property's electricity account. When the occupation of a property changes, the new bill-payer will take on responsibility for continuing the payments through their energy bills.

2.5.5   Draft regulations for the implementation of the Green Deal are expected in spring 2012 and it has been announced that the extension of the RHI to domestic property will be part of the package of proposals.

2.5.6   The Government is also working on reducing carbon emissions by aiming for "zero carbon" homes. It is likely that the forthcoming review of the Building Regulations will consider whether to introduce higher energy efficiency standards in building materials and construction techniques to assist in achieving these aims. Full relief from Stamp Duty Land Tax (SDLT) is currently available for certified zero-carbon homes costing less than £500,000. For properties costing more than £500,000, a deduction of up to £15,000 is made from the usual SDLT charge.

2.5.7   The Committee on Climate Change – an independent body charged with providing advice to the Government on carbon emissions and climate change – produced a Renewable Energy Review in May 2011. This sets out a pathway to achieve the target of a reduction in carbon emissions from heat of 80% by 2050 by suggesting that renewable heat needs to account for about 12% of heat demand by 2020 and 35% by 2030. The report recommends support for a mixture of technologies, including heat pumps, biomass boilers and biogas systems and emphasising the need for energy efficiency measures to be part of the package. It also recommends that steps are taken now to accredit suppliers in order to avoid bottlenecks in the next few years as confidence grows in the sector and more installations are developed.

2.5.8   In July 2011 the Government published the first UK Renewable Energy Roadmap, which is intended to be a plan for delivery of the policy targets, to be reviewed annually. The Roadmap identifies eight technologies which it believes can deliver more than 90% of the renewable energy needs of the UK by 2020. They are: onshore wind; offshore wind; marine energy; biomass electricity; biomass heat; ground source and air source heat pumps; and renewable transport. In considering renewable heat, the Roadmap estimates that by 2020, the RHI could deliver up to 24,000 biomass heat installations, generating up to 50 TWh of heat and 100,000 heat pumps, generating up to 22 TWh of heat.

2.6   UK Legislation

2.6.1   The statutory authority for the Renewable Heat Incentive is s.100 of the Energy Act 2008, which enables the Secretary of State to make regulations *"establishing a scheme to facilitate and encourage renewable generation of heat"*. The Renewable Heat Regulations themselves were first published in draft form in March 2011 and then laid in final form before Parliament in July 2011. They are expected to come into force with effect from 30th September 2011.

2.6.2   The Energy Act 2008 applies to England, Scotland and Wales, but not Northern Ireland, where decisions are made by the Assembly. As heat is a partially devolved issue in Scotland, the Energy Act made provision for Scottish Ministers to be consulted on the detail of the Regulations.

2.6.3   **The Energy Bill**, which is to apply to England, Wales and Scotland, is expected to be given Royal Assent in autumn 2011.

2.6.4   The Bill has three key objectives:
- To tackle barriers to investment in energy efficiency
- To enhance energy security
- To enable investment in low carbon energy supplies.

2.6.5   The key relevant parts of the Bill as it currently stands include The Green Deal – a new funding mechanism allowing domestic and non-domestic property occupiers to install energy efficient equipment or fittings which will be paid for out of energy bills. This is discussed in more detail at 11.0 below.

2.6.6   The Bill also makes amendments to the Energy Performance Certificate Regulations to allow wider disclosure of EPC data. Other changes to the EPC Regulations are proposed elsewhere as part of a review of the Regulations following the recast of the EPBD.

2.6.7   A review of energy efficiency in the private rented sector is included in the Bill, to start 12 months after the Green Deal commences (so in 2013) and covering both domestic and non-domestic property. This would compare the energy performance of the private rented sector with other sectors, assess available funding and consider the need to take action.

2.6.8   One of the potentially challenging provisions will enable new regulations which will require landlords to make or allow energy efficiency improvements in certain circumstances:

- Tenants' Energy Efficiency Regulations must be introduced before 1st April 2016 to require private landlords of domestic property to give consent to a request from tenants to implement energy efficiency savings in the let property.

- Energy Efficiency Regulations must be introduced before 1st April 2018 to require private landlords of domestic property to implement energy efficiency savings before the property is let, if it is below a specified energy efficiency rating.

- Non-domestic Energy Efficiency Regulations must be introduced before 1st April 2018 to require landlords of non-domestic property to implement energy efficiency savings before the property is let, if it is below a specified energy efficiency rating.

2.6.9   In each case the landlord will only have to carry out or permit the improvements if there will be no upfront cost, so the work can be carried out through the Green Deal or another financial arrangement permitted by the regulations.

2.6.10   Much detail will be left to the regulations, including the time period allowed to complete the improvements, the sanctions for failure to comply and the nature of any exemptions. Exemptions might be permitted because of a negative impact on the value of the property or because other consents or permissions are required and are not forthcoming (this might potentially include listed building consent, for example).

2.6.11   The central thrust of this part of the Energy Bill is to encourage property owners, including landlords, to make energy efficiency investments for which they should not have to pay significant initial costs, because funding will be available through the Green Deal. In effect, the occupiers who stand to benefit from improved energy efficiency will pay for the improvements through their energy bills. When the cost of the improvements has been recovered, the occupier's energy bills should fall and the landlords will have an improved property. While the repayments are being made, it is intended that the energy bills should be no higher than they were expected to be before the improvements were carried out. However, if landlords fail to act and the 2013 review shows that the private rented sector is lagging behind, there are powers to bring forward new regulations making it easier for tenants or local authorities to insist that improvements are made.

2.6.12   Scotland – The Climate Change (Scotland) Act 2009 led to the production of the Scottish Renewables Action Plan and the Renewable Heat Action Plan for Scotland, which sets out actions to achieve the target of 11% of Scotland's heat demand to come from renewable sources by 2020. The Renewables Action Plan was updated and expanded in 2011 and published as the 2020 Routemap for Renewable Energy in Scotland. Also in 2011, the Scottish Government issued its report "Low Carbon Scotland: Meeting the Emissions Reduction Targets 2010 – 2022: The Report on Proposals and Policies" which sets out annual targets for reducing emissions. In August 2011 Richard Lochhead announced that an Agri-Renewables Strategy was to be developed to support the emerging industry.

2.6.13   Wales – The Welsh Assembly Government's plans for Wales to meet almost all of its energy and heat needs from renewable sources by 2050 are set out in its 2010 energy statement 'A Low Carbon Revolution'.

2.7   Rural Property

2.7.1   While renewable heating systems will be attractive to many property owners and occupiers, they are likely to be of particular interest in rural areas where there are significant numbers of properties located off the mains gas grid, because the potential savings are greater when compared to the high cost of heating oil. Rural property is also more likely to have the necessary space to install a ground source heat pump or access to biomass for a boiler or anaerobic digestion (AD) system. The Government expects that the take up of the various incentives to support renewable heating systems will be greater in rural than in urban areas.

2.7.2   However, "retro-fitting" energy efficiency measures may be difficult to implement in older rural properties and listed buildings, especially those without cavity walls where the options for insulation might be limited to external or internal cladding, for example. Research carried out by BRE (formerly the Building Research Establishment) in 2008 estimated that over 2.3 million rural homes were classified as "hard to heat", primarily because they were off the gas-grid or had solid walls. The

Department of Communities and Local Government (DCLG) estimates that more than 20% of the current UK housing stock was built before 1919, when cavity walls were rare. It was not until after the Second World War that cavity wall construction became standard practice, but cavity insulation was only installed in about half the properties built.

2.8 Regulatory Bodies

2.8.1 The production of renewable heat is subject to a variety of regulatory regimes which are discussed at appropriate points in this paper. A summary of the main authorities is provided here with contact details given in Appendix II.

2.8.2 The main responsible UK ministry is the Department for Energy and Climate Change (DECC).

2.8.3 Ofgem (the Gas and Electricity Markets Authority) will administer the Renewable Heat Incentive Scheme, including responsibility for making payments.

2.8.4 The Environment Agency for England and Wales handles environmental licences for bioenergy, biomass, anaerobic digestion and open loop ground source heat pumps. These functions are handled in Scotland by the Scottish Environmental Protection Agency and in Northern Ireland by the Northern Ireland Environment Agency.

2.8.5 Development control for smaller schemes is the responsibility of local planning authorities. Once over certain thresholds national policies and procedures apply.

SECTION B: TECHNOLOGY

3. RENEWABLE HEAT TECHNOLOGIES ELIGIBLE FOR THE RHI

3.1   The technologies eligible for the RHI are defined in the Regulations:

3.1.1   Biomass boilers
- purpose designed and installed to generate heat from solid biomass only; or
- generating heat from solid biomass contained in municipal waste;

The use of fossil fuels (including peat) for burning or co-firing is not eligible for the RHI and nor is the use of bio-liquids, such as rapeseed oil and bio-diesel.

3.1.2   Heat pumps
- generating heat using naturally occurring energy from the ground (other than geothermal) or from surface water through an electrically powered heat pump, provided that the installation has a coefficient of performance of at least 2.9, meaning that it must produce at least 2.9 times more power than is used to run the system.

3.1.3   Solar thermal units
- generating heat captured from solar energy
- defined as "a liquid filled flat plate or evacuated tube solar collector", provided that the installation capacity is less than $200kW_{th}$.

3.1.4   Biogas
- generating heat using biogas produced from biomass by AD, gasification or pyrolysis, where the combustion of the biogas takes place in a separate plant from where it was produced and provided that the installation capacity is less than $200kW_{th}$.

3.1.5   Combined heat and power (CHP) units
- generating heat <u>and</u> power in the same unit from:
  - solid biomass
  - biogas with a capacity of less than $200kW_{th}$
  - deep geothermal.

3.1.6   Deep geothermal
- generating heat from naturally occurring sources at least 500m beneath the surface of the earth (deep geothermal heat systems).

Deep geothermal systems are currently under the ground source heat tariff which is unlikely to be attractive. A separate tariff may be developed in due course if further research shows that these systems can be viable in the UK.

3.2   Other technologies
Other renewable heat technologies are not eligible for the RHI as it currently stands, although some may be brought into the scheme in future, if their efficiency can be proven to DECC's satisfaction.
- Air source heat pumps – a likely candidate to be brought in for domestic systems from 2012, but currently there are problems in metering output.
- Direct air heating
- Larger solar thermal systems
- Larger biogas systems
- Bioliquids.

3.3   Cooling
Heat used for cooling (for example, through the use of absorption chillers) will be eligible for the RHI if it meets all the criteria of the scheme, but such technology is too expensive at the current time for widespread use. The use of heat pumps to provide cooling will not be eligible for the RHI, as this does not count towards renewable targets under the EU Renewable Energy Directive.

3.4   Heating for Processes
3.4.1   The use of heat in a process is an eligible use under the Regulations and an obvious example of where this might be of interest to farmers is for grain drying. Biomass boilers designed to run on farm by-products such as straw and crop waste could offer a viable alternative to oil-fired systems.

3.4.2   The only case where process heat is not eligible for RHI payments is for heat used in the anaerobic digestion process, such as heat used to warm a digester or pasteurise food waste. Such heat is known as parasitic heat load and is not eligible for RHI payments.

3.5   Scale
3.5.1   The scale of a heat generating project is referred to by its maximum potential generating capacity, so a $100kW_{th}$ scheme should generate 100kW of heat per hour when operating under optimum conditions. Different technologies operate at different efficiency rates.

3.5.2   Appendix V sets out further information on heat measurement and scale.

4. BIOMASS BOILERS

4.1 Introduction

Today's biomass-powered boilers are the modern version of what is probably the oldest form of heating known to man – the burning of plant-derived material. Biomass-powered boilers are particularly suitable where the property owner also controls the supply of biomass, thus providing a degree of energy security. Wood burning stoves are excluded from the RHI at present, due to concerns about their efficiency, difficulties in monitoring output and the fact that many can also be run on fossil fuels.

4.2 Planning a Biomass Boiler Heating System

The general issues which need to be considered when planning a renewable heating system are discussed in some detail at paragraph 15.0. If a biomass boiler system is planned, the following questions also need to be addressed:

- What type of fuel will be used?
  - Where will it come from?
  - Is there a secure supply?
  - What will the processing, storage and handling requirements be?
  - How will it be delivered to the site?
  - Is there an issue over air quality?
- What number and type of properties are being heated?
  - Is it a district heating scheme?
  - What is the heat demand?
- What type of boiler is needed?
  - What size and capacity?
  - Does it need to be able to burn other fuels?
  - What will the ongoing maintenance costs be?
- How should the system be designed?
  - Where will the boiler be situated?
  - Is there good access and room for a fuel bunker?
  - How will the boiler connect to the end user?
  - What are the back-up arrangements?

4.3 What type of fuel?

4.3.1 'Biomass' is defined by the OECD Glossary of Statistical Terms as *"any plant matter used directly as fuel or converted into other forms before combustion"*.

4.3.2 In the UK this generally means:
- Wood – either in the form of virgin wood as a by-product of commercial timber production; through the active management of small woods to produce coppice or thinnings; or treated wood recovered through recycling schemes;
- Short rotation coppice grown specifically as fuel crops – including willow, poplar, miscanthus and reed canary grass;
- Agricultural products – principally straw, but potentially also sugar beet, maize or grain starch;
- Biomass from municipal waste – i.e. the bio-degradable element of waste that would otherwise be disposed of in landfill. This is a specialist area due to the stringent requirements of the Waste Incineration Directive, but it has been taken up by some local authorities to run district heating schemes.

4.3.3 The raw material is usually processed for ease of handling, either by baling, chipping or pelleting. The processing, treatment and subsequent storage can have a significant effect on the quality of the final product. Consistency of the end product can be important in the efficient operation of the system and careful consideration needs to be given to the source of the fuel before making a final decision on the type of boiler. Ideally the fuel source should be considered at the earliest stage of planning a biomass boiler scheme, as many boilers will be designed and set up to run most efficiently on a particular fuel and output may be adversely affected by changes.

4.3.4   With this issue of consistency in mind, European standards are being developed for biomass. The CEN/TC 335 Biomass Standards have been adopted by BSI British Standards and cover topics such as methods for defining the calorific value of biomass fuels, determining moisture content or defining chip size. Many biomass systems will now specify the required fuel type by reference to these standards to ensure optimum performance.

4.3.5   The Carbon Trust has prepared templates for contracts for the supply of biomass fuel and for the supply of renewable heat. They can be downloaded from the Carbon Trust website at: http://www.carbontrust.co.uk/emerging-technologies/current-focus-areas/biomass/ pages/biomass-resources.aspx

4.3.6   Clean Air Act – The application of the Clean Air Act may prevent the use of biomass boilers in some locations. The Clean Air Act 2003 consolidated and updated previous legislation designed to control the amount of smoke released into the atmosphere. The Act allows local authorities to declare "smoke control areas" where the only fuels that may be burnt are those authorised by the Act. Smoke Control Areas can include rural locations, especially in regions of former industrial activity, such as the East Midlands and West Yorkshire. The areas can be on a street-by-street basis and it is necessary to check with the relevant local authority to establish whether or not a property lies within one.

4.3.7   It is an offence to burn an unauthorised fuel in a smoke control area unless in an exempt appliance. DEFRA's website has a Smoke Control section which includes lists of authorised fuel and exempt appliances by brand name and description for England, Scotland, Wales and Northern Ireland. An exempt appliance may only be used to burn the fuel specified in the DEFRA list.

4.3.8   There is no general exemption for biomass fuels, such as wood chip, wood pellets, miscanthus or straw, none of which is an authorised fuel under the Act. This means that if they are to be burned in a Smoke Control Area they must be used in an exempt appliance and in accordance with the use restrictions.

4.4   Security of fuel supply
4.4.1   Part of the attraction of a renewable heat system is the ability to secure control over the heat source, so that properties off the gas grid are not reliant on expensive, imported oil. However, biomass boilers can be suitable for use in properties such as schools and small private houses which do not have access to their own supply of woodchip or other fuel. In these cases it will be important to consider how the supply of fuel is to be sourced at the earliest stage of the project, in order to minimise exposure to the vagaries of the open market. If the project is of sufficient scale, it may be possible to seek supply contracts for a period of years to minimise the risk. The RHI could lead to a rise in demand for woodchip and other fuels and it is yet to be seen how the supply side of the equation will respond.

4.4.2   The market for and price of woodchips has already risen substantially with growing interest in this sector, especially from substantial power stations. The current price of around £80/tonne for woodchips at 30% dry matter still offers a substantial cost advantage over oil. If several larger wood burning power stations are taken forward they could rapidly require far more chips than may be available in the United Kingdom, but may anyway prefer to import on cost grounds.

4.4.3   While there is much relatively unmanaged woodland, it is not yet clear that a suitable volume of woodchips will be consistently available over a twenty year period.

4.4.4   The Forestry Commission in England has published a Woodfuel Implementation Plan which sets out how it intends to support the emerging woodfuel supply chain in England. Scotland and Wales both have dedicated websites for the woodfuel sector – www.usewoodfuel.co.uk for Scotland and www.woodfuelwales.org.uk for Wales.

4.4.5   These issues all point to wood burning being especially attractive to properties that control a sufficient area of woodland to self-supply a project rather than being reliant on buying feedstock.

4.5   Woodchip: self-supply
4.5.1   Woodchip may be derived from forestry by-products; traditional coppice, such as sweet chestnut or hazel; or short rotation coppice such as willow or poplar. Some estates are reviving rotations of coppice to provide a sustainable source of woodchip, while others have been drawn to biomass schemes in part by the need to find an economic use for forestry by-products. Setting up an in-house supply enterprise can work well if there is a large enough area of woodland to supply a sufficient quantity of consistent material for the boiler. Figures from the Forestry Commission's Biomass Energy Centre suggest that one hectare of woodchip from thinnings can produce 10.3MWh of output.

4.5.2   Typically, chip wood will be harvested and stacked at the rideside or roadside to begin the drying out process in the round, which might take up to two years. It will then be transferred to a chipping site to be chipped and stored. Softwood chip has both a lower calorific value and a lower density than hardwood chip, meaning that more storage space will be required for softwood to deliver the same amount of heat as hardwood. Probably of greater significance, though, are both moisture content and chip size (long shards of wood can block augers, for example) and the supply process should be planned and managed to deliver as consistent an end product as possible. Moisture should be below 30% in most cases as wetter fuel will generate less heat per tonne, although the capabilities of boilers to handle fuel at different moisture contents do vary.

4.5.3   As the chip wood can take up to two years to dry out at rideside, it is important to plan the supply side of the operation at the earliest stages of the project so that a sufficient supply of suitable chip will be available by the time that the boiler is ready to be commissioned.

4.5.4   To develop a supply enterprise, the basic requirements will be:
- outside storage space for unprocessed timber
- access to a chipper, which might be hired in on an occasional basis
- covered storage for chippings
- tractor or handler for loading.

4.5.5   Care should be taken with the storage of large quantities of woodchip, as heaps can either compost or combust under certain conditions. Heaps may need to be mixed to ensure that moisture is uniform throughout the heap, but care should be taken to ensure that stones do not become incorporated into the heap as these can damage augers. There may also be a risk of arson if heaps are accessible.

4.5.6   Where there is an in-hand supply, some estates will seek to set a price on woodchip for internal accounting purposes or when different departments operate as separate profit centres. In other cases this may not be deemed necessary.

4.5.7   Woodchip – sourced externally
4.5.8   If the woodchip is to be sourced externally, careful research should be carried out at an early stage of planning the project in order to establish that there are suitable suppliers in the locality and to assess the terms available for a supply contract. Woodchip supplies over which the property owner has no control are subject to all the same vagaries of supply, demand and market price as are heating oil or gas.

4.5.9   The quality of chip is very important to the efficient working of the boiler and can make a considerable difference to the running costs of the system, not just in respect of heat output per tonne, but also in breakdown time and repair costs. It is therefore important to establish that a supplier is reliable and will produce a consistent product of known quality. Just as in any other commercial arrangement, the appropriate due diligence steps should be taken to assess the suitability of the suppliers who are asked to tender for a contract.

4.5.10   Prices to supply woodchip might be quoted per tonne or per kilowatt hour. A contract to supply a specified number of kilowatt hours will incentivise the supplier to send good quality, dry chip, as this will mean fewer loads to be delivered. On the other hand, a contract to supply a fixed number of tonnes might provide an incentive to send fewer loads of wetter, heavier chip. A heat meter will be necessary to measure the heat produced by the supplied fuel, but heat meters are in any case a requirement if the Renewable Heat Incentive payments are to be claimed.

4.5.11   Those heating commercial premises are likely to seek longer supply contracts to provide a degree of security. Terms of three to five years are not uncommon, with the tender price index-linked over the term.

4.6   Wood pellets
4.6.1   Wood pellets are formed from waste wood products, including sawdust, bark and woodchip. Pellets will bind without additives due to the natural lignin in the wood, but maize starch or vegetable oils are sometimes used in the production process.

4.6.2   Pellets have the advantages of being more uniform in size than woodchip and easier to handle because they will "flow". This means that they can be blown into stores in the same way as animal feed if bulk storage areas are available. They are also of higher density and lower moisture than woodchip, meaning that a smaller volume should provide a greater amount of heat, all other things being equal. They should also produce less ash than woodchip. Disadvantages of pellets include a propensity for them to disintegrate when wet or if handled too roughly.

4.6.3   The market for UK manufactured pellets is developing rapidly and there are a number of UK manufacturers offering bulk delivery or pallet deliveries for smaller schemes. Prices being asked in April 2011 ranged from £166.50 per tonne delivered for bulk supplies to £245 per tonne delivered for a one tonne pallet of small (10kg or 20kg) bags.

4.6.4   Storage and handling systems for wood pellets need to be carefully designed to take into account their friability. They must be dry and weatherproof so that pellets do not get wet. If pellets are to be blown into a store, pipes should be straight with angles minimised, as sharp corners tend to lead to pellet fracture. Impact damage in the store can be minimised to some extent by plastic hanging curtains or sheeted bunker walls.

4.7   Straw

4.7.1   Many types of plant straw are suitable for use in biomass boilers. Wheat, barley and oat straw can also be used, but might have a higher value to the farm as animal feed or bedding. Oilseed rape and bean straws, however, are low value by-products well suited to use in biomass boilers. A study carried out in 2003 for the New and Renewable Energy Programme in the Department of Trade and Industry found that there was little difference in the calorific value of cereal straw and oilseed rape straw, although the latter tends to burn hotter due to oil residues (*A Trial Burn of Rape Straw and Whole Crops Harvested for Energy Use to Assess Efficiency Implications*, November 2003). In power station trials oilseed rape straw was co-fired with cereal straw to reduce this volatility.

4.7.2   Straw will have a typical moisture content of 15 – 25%, depending on conditions at harvest and during storage. Figures from the Forestry Commission's Biomass Energy Centre suggest that one hectare of wheat straw providing 3.7 tonnes of dry matter can produce 17MWh of output and a report for the National Non-Food Crops Centre estimates that straw has an energy content of around 5MWh per dry tonne (*Evaluation of Opportunities for Converting Indigenous UK Wastes to Fuels and Energy*, July 2009).

4.7.3   Straw for fuel can be grown as part of a normal crop rotation and many farms will already have (or use contractors who have) the equipment and facilities for baling, handling, storing and transporting it. The removal of straw from the land on a regular basis means that it is not available for incorporation into the soil, with potential consequences for soil structure and fertility which might need to be taken into account when preparing costings. These consequences might be mitigated in part if it is possible to return the ash from the boiler back to the land.

4.7.4   If straw-based heating systems become popular, there might be a consequent revival of interest in longer-strawed varieties of cereal to meet the demand.

4.8   Miscanthus (Elephant grass)

4.8.1   Miscanthus is a perennial grass from Asia which grows from rhizomes to produce dense clumps of stems. Like maize and sugar cane, it is in a class of plants which use a C4 photosynthetic pathway, which means that it uses carbon dioxide much more efficiently to produce a greater mass than more typical temperate plants can do. It is estimated that although less than 4% of plants use the C4 pathway, they account for about 20% of all plant growth.

4.8.2   Rhizomes are planted in late spring using bespoke planters and the crop takes two or three years to become established, reaching full potential by year five. Good weed control is essential during this time. Establishment costs are in the region of £1200/ha.

4.8.3   Once established, the crop requires no fertiliser and little in the way of weed control, as it forms a dense canopy. The only significant annual cost is the cost of harvesting, which is carried out between January and March, when the plant has died back leaving only bamboo-like canes which are cut and baled using a normal large square baler. It requires little, if any, drying. The plant will grow again from March onwards and well established crops can yield up to 20 t/ha per year. The winter harvesting period means that miscanthus should be planted in drier locations if possible. It will tolerate most soils but the better the soil, the better the performance.

4.8.4   Because it is not particularly deep-rooted, miscanthus can be removed by harvesting the rhizomes and is easier to clear from the land than most types of short rotation coppice, for example.

4.8.5   Figures from the Forestry Commission's Biomass Energy Centre suggest that one hectare of miscanthus yielding about 13 tonnes of dry matter can produce 63MWh of output.

4.9   Energy crops and sustainability

4.9.1   The DECC policy document 'Renewable Heat' sets out concerns about sustainability of feedstock for biomass boilers. Biomass schemes with a capacity of $1MW_{th}$ and over will have to report quarterly to Ofgem on the sustainability of their feedstock.

4.9.2   The policy document statement on energy crops grown for use in AD plants is set out below:

> *"Use of energy crops*
>
> *As stated in the Waste Framework Directive, Government policy is to specifically deliver an increase in energy from waste through AD. We recognise that, at farm scale, some energy crops may be required in combination with slurries and that such crops can be grown as part of the normal agricultural rotation. Furthermore, there is land available which is not suitable for the production of food crops but which may, therefore, be used to supply energy-crop only AD plants. It is not our policy, however, to encourage energy crops–based AD, particularly where these are grown to the exclusion of food producing crops. If evidence shows that there is a large scale use of crops in AD and a resulting conversion or change in land used for crops to support AD, then measures will be considered to address this. DECC and Defra will discuss how such a mechanism could work in practice. The Government will, therefore, be investigating possible measures to exclude from RHI support, the large scale use of energy crops in AD."*

4.9.3   The spring 2011 DECC consultation on a review of the Feed-in Tariff for small scale AD plants also raised the question of energy crops and the scale of their use. This would appear to be an area of concern for the Government and it is possible that restrictions on energy crop use could be introduced in future. It may also be a concern for lenders who would not wish to be seen to be funding potentially controversial schemes.

4.10   What Type of Boiler is Needed?

4.10.1   Biomass boilers are available to suit a wide range of systems, from a single domestic dwelling system of, say, 15kW, to large scale commercial systems of up to 5MW. The basic principle is that fuel is fed into the system, where it is burned in a controlled environment to extract the maximum heat energy. The hot gas passes either through a turbine to produce electricity, or more usually through a heat exchanger to heat water, which can then be pumped into a central heating system.

4.10.2   Boilers fall into two main types:
- Continuous flow systems, which take in a supply of fuel (chip or pellets) at a rate to match the demands on the system. These can be further sub-divided into moving grate, plane grate or stoker burner systems. Moving grate systems are the most versatile and can handle a variety of fuel types at higher moisture content, but tend to be the most expensive option. Stoker burners are the most basic and least expensive of the three, with plane grate systems as the middle option.
- Batch systems are suitable for baled fuel or logs, when the boiler is loaded up on a regular basis. They are less sophisticated and less expensive than continuous flow boilers, but require more frequent and regular management. Because batch systems are not burning in response to demand, they require large thermal storage tanks so that reserves of hot water can be held.

4.10.3   In either type of system the ash residue must be disposed of. This is collected automatically in some systems while others rely on manual ash removal. While boiler manufacturers will often claim that mechanically collected ash will be cold, this is not always the case and ash receptacles should be carefully designed to minimise any risk of fire.

4.10.4   The boiler will require regular routine servicing and maintenance and a servicing contract may be part of the package agreed on installation. As many boilers are made in Europe, spare parts are not always available in the UK at short notice and so some installers recommend keeping essential spare parts in stock. This will be especially important where there is no back-up heating system in place, but inevitably comes at a cost.

4.11   System capacity
4.11.1   Detailed calculations to determine the system capacity and the appropriate size of the boiler will normally be done by a specialist consultant. The basic approach is firstly to estimate the current heat use and then consider how the boiler can meet it. The current heat use should ideally be measured over the course of a year, so that seasonal and other variations can be taken into account, either by monitoring the use of the current heat source (e.g. heating oil), or by installing a heat meter with data logging capabilities. For new buildings, the information will have to be estimated by reference to standard data. It will be important to understand whether the stated output figures will actually be delivered and those factors which may affect that.

4.11.2   To consider how the boiler can meet the heat use, it is then necessary to decide whether the boiler will cover the base load only, or the peak load of heat. Modern biomass boilers are said to work at useful efficiencies when the required output is between 30% and 100% of maximum load, but to be less efficient when the heat demand is variable or below 30%. The base load is the minimum amount of heat which is demanded throughout the year. If the boiler is designed to meet this load then it will operate at a steady continual rate, but a secondary heating system – such as a back-up oil boiler – may be required at peak times. In some cases, a smaller biomass boiler runs through the year with a larger one used for spring and autumn and both together in the winter.

4.11.3   A boiler designed to meet the peak load will be running at over-capacity whenever the load is below the peak point and for this reason it is best suited to situations when demand is fairly consistent throughout the year.

4.11.4   In practice, it is most likely that a point between the base load and peak load will be identified so that the boiler is providing the bulk of the heat throughout the year, but may need a top-up system in place for times of very high demand. Additional heat stores in the form of water tanks may help to smooth out peaks and troughs in daily demand, giving a reserve buffer.

4.12   System design

4.12.1   The hot water from a biomass boiler can be fed into an existing heating system through existing pipes and radiators. In smaller and more modern properties this may be a matter of a relatively straightforward connection, either direct to a biomass boiler or, in a district heating system, via a heat exchanger to each property.

4.12.2   Older properties can present more difficulties and these can be further compounded if the building is listed. Old pipework, chimneys and fittings will not necessarily be suitable for the new system and in listed properties it may be difficult to find suitable housing for the boiler. Poor insulation in older and larger properties can make it difficult to establish the appropriate heating requirements in order to select a boiler of the right capacity. The advice of an experienced building surveyor or consultant may be required at an early stage.

4.12.3   The boiler itself can be housed some distance from the properties it is to heat, provided that insulated pipes can be laid between sites. The boiler house should provide:
   - easy access to the boiler for routine maintenance, repair and ash removal
   - a fuel bunker which is dry and large enough to keep the boiler supplied
   - good access and adequate overhead clearance to facilitate re-filling the bunker.

4.12.4   The fuel delivery mechanism should be as simple as possible to reduce the risk of breakdowns. The three main options are:
   - An agitator arm which sweeps chip or pellets into the auger for delivery to the boiler – simple and widely used;
   - A walking floor system to shuffle chip or pellets into an auger – can put stresses on the bunker walls and has more moving parts and hence more risk of failure;
   - A conveyor belt or mechanical grab system delivering directly to the boiler – best suited to larger systems or those using baled fuel.

4.13   Illustrative Costs

4.13.1   The costs below are given for illustrative purposes only, as each project will have unique characteristics which bear on the design, construction and running costs. They set the RHI against the capital cost in a partial budget. A full calculation will require consideration of the full running costs, including maintenance and servicing, alongside the savings made – as this heat will often be substituting for power bought in at market prices.

4.13.2   The cost of a small scale boiler of 20kW heating a property equivalent to a typical three bedroom house is likely to be in the region of £10,000 – £12,000. The potential output of the boiler is a function of its capacity and the running hours. A 20kW boiler installed in a commercial property might run for 2000 hours per year, generating 40,000kWh of heat. Under the RHI, the first 1,314 hours would be paid at 7.9p and the remainder at 2.0p. Annual income from the RHI would be:

1,314 x 20kW = 26,280kWh @ 7.9p =   £2,076.12
686 x 20kW = 13,720kWh @ 2.0p =   £274.40
Total annual RHI income =   £2,350.52
So the RHI will surpass the capital cost in about six years.

4.13.3   A district heating scheme on a rural estate in southern England with 16,000 square feet of offices, conference venue and residential accommodation installed a 240kW boiler in 2009 at a cost of just over £180,000 before grants; installed before the RHI was announced, it attracted some regional development funding. It is estimated that it will take three to four years at current oil prices for the cost of the boiler to be covered, which is consistent with anecdotal reports from other rural estates.

4.13.4   Under the RHI, a 240kW boiler providing year-round heat and hot water, running for 7,300 hours per year would generate:

1,314 x 240kW = 315,360kWh @ 4.9p =   £15,452.64
5,986 x 240kW = 1,436,640kWh @ 2.0p =   £28,732.80
Total annual RHI income =   £44,185.44
So the RHI surpasses the capital cost of the boiler in about five years. Note that for a district heating scheme, the additional costs of pipes and heat exchangers would need to be considered.

4.13.5   The annual running costs of new biomass boilers are estimated to be about 40% of those of the oil fired boilers, depending on the relative costs of heating oil and biomass fuel.

5. HEAT PUMPS

5.1   Ground and water source heat pump systems use the latent heat in the ground, or under water, to provide a constant source of heat which can be boosted to a useful temperature through a pump. They require a sufficient area of land or water to lay the pipes and room to install a heat pump in the building, but there are none of the issues of securing a fuel supply which are so important to biomass systems.

5.2   Air source heat pumps use similar principles to extract heat from the air, but as these are not currently eligible for the RHI, they are not considered further in this publication.

5.3   The system operates by capturing the latent heat in the ground or under water using fluid circulating through a pipe. Even at relatively shallow depths below ground, the average annual temperature will be close to 10°C and the temperature of the fluid, which is usually water with antifreeze, is raised by a few degrees. Using technology often described as being similar to that found in a domestic refrigerator (but in reverse), this then passes through a heat exchanger to warm a refrigerant with a low boiling point which evaporates, absorbing heat energy. It is then compressed, which raises the temperature and pressure, returning the refrigerant to liquid form. The hot liquid then passes through another heat exchanger and warms the water which circulates in the heating system. There are three circulating sealed loops: the heat source fluid circulating through the ground (or water), the refrigerant fluid inside the heat pump and the hot water in the heating system.

5.4   The heat pumps themselves require electricity to make them work, at a cost and larger systems may require a three phase supply. In circumstances when the renewable nature of the energy is important to the consumer, the electricity could come from a renewable source itself, such as small scale hydro, or a wind turbine or solar photovoltaic array on site (although these will be less consistent in supply), or through a 'green' supply contract with an electricity provider.

5.5   For closed loop systems – where the heat source pipes are sealed and heat exchange takes place through the pipe – the heat source pipes can be laid in either ground or water.

5.6   Water source systems require a suitably sized body of water which should be close enough to the buildings to minimise heat loss between the two. The heat source pipes can be laid on the bottom of ponds and lakes, but there should be an inflow and outflow to ensure moving water to maximise the efficiency of the system and avoid any cooling of the water body. Water sources avoid the need for expensive and disruptive groundworks, but it may be necessary to dredge the pond or lake before installing the pipes.

5.7   Ground source systems rely on the pipes being buried, at least one metre and sometimes up to two metres below the surface in trenches, or, where there is insufficient space, sunk in boreholes. The ground can be reinstated, but records should be kept of where the pipes are laid for future reference. Pipes should be below the likely frost level and laid deep enough to avoid being accidentally pulled up by disturbance to the ground above. The pipes can have a life expectancy of 20 years or more. Ground source systems can be more expensive to install if very long trenches are required and the cost is likely to increase significantly if boreholes have to be drilled.

5.8   Pipes are laid in loops and the length of pipe needed will depend on the size of the system installed, but generally the longer the pipes, the better. They can be conventional pipes (needing long, but narrow trenches) or so-called 'slinky' pipes which are laid in a horizontal spiral coil (needing wide but shorter trenches). The actual capacity of the system will usually be assessed by a specialist contractor working with the equipment supplier. Wet ground conditions will assist heat transfer and are preferable to very dry ground.

5.9   An alternative is an 'open loop' system, where ground water is abstracted from an aquifer or river and circulated through the heat source pipes before being returned to the water source. Open loop systems require Environment Agency (or Scottish Environment Protection Agency – SEPA) consents for abstraction and discharge (see paragraph 16.2).

5.10   There have been some concerns about how efficient heat pumps are, given that electricity is required to run them. Their performance is assessed by using a Coefficient of Performance, measured as the heating output divided by the total power consumed by the system, including fans, pumps and controls. This must be greater than 2.9 for the technology to be eligible for the RHI, i.e. the system must produce at least 2.9 times more energy than it consumes. The European Standard for heat pump performance is EN 14511.

5.11   Most heat pump systems can only heat water to about 55°C but are more efficient at lower temperatures. They also tend to be slow to reach operating temperature, so in order to maximise efficiency, buildings should have:
   • Excellent insulation to minimise heat loss
   • Underfloor heating with a solid surface, such as tile or stone
   • Constant circulation systems so that the pumps are not being switched on and off.

5.12   However, heat pumps can also work with larger bore radiators in environments where a constant but lower heat is preferable. Local secondary heating might be required, such as wood-fired stoves in a domestic environment.

5.13   Hot water for washing and bathing needs to be regularly heated to more than 60°C to reduce the risk from legionella bacteria, so either the system must be set to manage this, or a booster heat source may need to be added for hot water supplies.

5.14   Installing an underfloor heating system is very disruptive in existing buildings, but is an option that can work well for new builds, substantial rebuilding projects or conversions, when good insulation can be installed into the floors, walls and roofs at the same time. Underfloor systems bring their own maintenance difficulties as they are frequently installed with solid floors which will store and radiate the heat. In these circumstances, a leaking pipe can cause major disruption and cost if the floor has to be lifted and fully dried out and so precautions against frost damage during construction and if buildings are empty during cold weather will be particularly important.

5.15   A reversible pump could also supply cooling, but this will not be eligible for RHI payments.

5.16   The Environment Agency has issued an Environmental Good Practice Guide for Ground Source Heating and Cooling aimed at developers and installers, which sets out what needs to be done to meet environmental regulation and manage environmental risks. The Guide can be downloaded from the Environment Agency website or requested in hard copy.

5.17   Illustrative costs

5.17.1   The costs below are given for illustrative purposes only, as each project will have unique characteristics which bear on the design, construction and running costs.

5.17.2   A typical domestic scale system is likely to be between 10 and 20kW, with an output of say 3500kW$_{th}$ per year. Such a system could cost in the region of £10 – 12,000 before the cost of groundworks, which can be considerable; if using slinky coils, approximately ten metres of trench is needed per kilowatt of load. RHI payments at 4.5p/kW$_{th}$, will not pay for the cost of installation over the twenty year life of the scheme, but cost savings against heating oil are said to be significant.

5.17.3   Castle Howard in Yorkshire installed a water source heat pump in 2009 at a cost (before grants) of approximately £185,000. The system connects to existing, large bore radiators in the house and the lower, but more constant, level of heat was found to be particularly suitable for the collection of art and artefacts. The system is estimated to have reduced CO_2 emissions by about 60%. Total heating and hot water costs for 2010 were approximately 36% of those in 2008.

6. SOLAR THERMAL UNITS

6.1   Solar thermal units are primarily found in the form of solar collectors for heating hot water. Domestic water heating accounts for about 7% of total UK energy use and 24% of domestic energy use, so there is an opportunity for solar thermal units to make a contribution, but they are frequently quoted as being able to provide only about half of the hot water needed for a domestic system in the UK. In our temperate climate, most will be unable to heat water to more than 60oC, which is the minimum temperature to which hot water for washing and bathing must be heated to reduce the risk to health from legionella bacteria, so a secondary heat source will be needed in almost all cases.

6.2   The technology is well established, but generation is limited in the UK because although typical solar radiation of $4 - 5.4kW_{th}/m^2$ can be expected in July, in December the figure will be close to $0.6kW_{th}/m^2$. There is therefore a mismatch with the demand for space heating, which will be lowest in the summer months of peak solar radiation. In hotter countries the technology is much more common; in Israel, for example, it is said to account for 80% of domestic energy requirements.

6.3   Of the various options, two types of solar thermal unit are in common use: flat plate collectors and evacuated tube systems. Each will comprise a collector panel to absorb solar radiation, which is usually roof-mounted on south facing aspects and should be unshaded for maximum efficiency. Other requirements are a storage tank for hot water and a system for circulating the hot water around the property, either pumped or gravity-fed.
- Flat plate collectors comprise liquid-carrying tubes (often copper for good conductivity) beneath a black painted cover (to maximise heat absorption) with a glass cover for protection. They tend to be more simple and cheaper, but less efficient, than the evacuated tubes.
- Evacuated tube systems use a series of glass tubes with a heat pipe in which a heat transfer fluid is vaporised at low temperatures, then linked to circulating water through a heat exchanger. These tend to be more efficient in less sunny climes like the UK.

6.4   In both cases the heat-absorbing liquid in the collector panel should include an anti-freeze. The life expectancy of the panels is expected to be around 25 years, but actual life will depend in part on the siting of the panels and their exposure to fluctuations in temperature.

6.5   Solar collectors are suitable for retro-fitting to existing buildings, but this is most likely to be as part of an overhaul of the water heating system, as a new hot water cylinder may be required. Installation costs can, therefore, be quite high, but this is off-set by generally low running costs and a free source of renewable heat. Roof top installations require the roof to be structurally capable of taking the load of the installation. The expected lifespan of the roof covering should be the same as or longer than the solar system, otherwise any unplanned maintenance to the roof covering will require an expensive reinstallation of the solar collectors.

6.6   There are many factors to consider in the design of a system heated using solar collectors, including:
- the size and siting of the hot water cylinder;
- whether direct or indirect circulation is used;
- whether systems are pumped or gravity-fed;
- ensuring that all parts are properly insulated to minimise heat loss.

6.7   The efficiency of a solar thermal system will depend on its latitude and orientation. In the north of Scotland, one square metre of solar collector panels is reported to generate around $900kW_{th}$ per year, rising to about $1,250kW_{th}$ per year in the south west of England (Renewable Energy Association).

6.8   Illustrative costs

6.8.1   The costs below are given for illustrative purposes only, as each project will have unique characteristics which bear on the design, construction and running costs.

6.8.2   Typical costs for installing solar collectors on a domestic property are between £3,000 and £5,000 for a system covering $3 - 4m^2$ producing, say, $3,500kW_{th}$ per year. This excludes any additional cost for re-configuring the existing heating system or installing additional hot water cylinders. With an RHI payment rate of 8.5p per kW_{th}, the annual payment will be £297.50 and thus it will take more than 10 years to pay for even the cheapest system from the RHI payment alone, excluding savings from spending less on other sources of heat. Some property owners might consider that the money would be better spent on improving insulation.

7. BIOGAS

7.1   Biogas is gas produced from renewable sources by one of several processes:
- anaerobic digestion – breaking down non-woody biomass and other organic matter in the absence of oxygen;
- gasification – treating biomass (or fossil fuels) at very high temperatures to break it down into carbon monoxide, carbon dioxide, hydrogen and methane;
- pyrolysis – the thermochemical decomposition of biomass in the absence of oxygen (similar to the process which produces charcoal);
- sewage gas – produced through the digestion and incineration of sewage sludge.

7.2   The gases produced by these processes can be used in several ways:
- to power turbines to provide electricity (eligible for FiTs);
- to burn as a source of renewable heat in a local system (eligible for RHI);
- in combined heat and power plants producing both electricity (eligible for FiTs) and heat (eligible for RHI);
- to inject into the national gas grid after treatment (eligible for RHI).

7.3   The process most likely to be encountered by agricultural valuers is anaerobic digestion, as plants are frequently sited on farms or rely on farmland for the disposal of digestate. CAAV Numbered Publication 203 – The On-Farm Generation of Renewable Electricity – describes the anaerobic digestion process in detail.

7.4   If the digester is operating properly each tonne of dry matter used should produce 200-400m3 biogas at 50 to 75% methane and an average energy output of 2.2MW$_{th}$. The gas is stored either on top of the digester in an inflatable container or in a tank next to the plant.

7.5   The typical composition of biogas from digestion is:
- Methane – 50 to 75%, about 55% for biogas from silage maize due to its carbohydrate content
- Carbon dioxide – 25 to 50%
- Nitrogen – nil to 10%
- Hydrogen sulphide – nil to 3%, lower from fodder beet
- Oxygen – nil to 2%
- Hydrogen – nil to 1%
- a little ammonia
- a little water vapour.

Biogas from gasifying wood and other biomass has a different composition, with little methane, its fuel value lying in hydrogen and carbon monoxide.

7.6   The biogas may need to be cleaned, by some form of biogas upgrading, before it can be used as a fuel. The Environment Agency sets strict limits on the hydrogen sulphide content of gases, which is toxic and corrosive to machinery. This can be removed by technologies such as amine gas treatment. Adding ferrous chloride to the digester can inhibit the production of hydrogen sulphide. Other contaminants may also need to be considered and particulates may need to be filtered out.

7.7   If it is to be injected into the natural gas grid it must be scrubbed to remove impurities and to ensure that its calorific value closely matches that of the natural gas in the network. All hydrogen sulphide, carbon dioxide, water and particulates must be removed to leave at least a 96% methane content. The EU Guideline for equalising biogas and natural gas required that biogas must be allowed into the gas network provided it does not cause any technical problems or compromise of security. As the regulatory framework appears complex to those outside it, Biomethane into the Gas Network: A Guide for Producers was published by DECC as guidance in December 2009.

7.8   Those who inject gas into the grid may need a Gas Transporter's Licence. DECC is consulting on whether an exemption from these regulations can be made for those enterprises whose main business is not in gas transport.

7.9   The operation of the gas market means that consumers choose the gas they buy; the network's task is simply to transport equivalent volumes.

7.10   Biogas can be burnt in gas boilers, but it must be treated first to remove hydrogen sulphide otherwise this can oxidise to form sulphuric acid, which will corrode the boiler. Excess water vapour and particulates can also be removed to improve operational efficiency.

7.11   Heat generated from burning biogas can be used to warm the digester and pasteurise food waste, referred to as parasitic heat load. This is not an eligible use for the RHI. In an anaerobic digestion CHP unit, the parasitic heat load can account for up to 30% of the heat produced.

8. DEEP GEOTHERMAL SYSTEMS

8.1   Deep geothermal systems rely on extracting heat from far below the surface of the earth – as much as 500 metres below in the UK – usually by either extracting from reservoirs of hot water, or by pumping cold water into the earth to be heated. This is the only major source of non-fossil fuel energy that is effectively independent of the sun. Temperature rises with depth (the centre of the earth is said to be around 7,000°C) and additional heat is generated by the decay of radioactive isotopes in the upper crust.

8.2   It has been especially exploited in areas where the geology offers high "enthalpy", a combination of temperature, pressure and volume, mostly associated with tectonic activity and volcanic areas. Thus, significant geothermal energy (for electricity as well as heat) is managed in Indonesia, Mexico, the Philippines and the USA, while it provides 10% of New Zealand's power. The Larderello power station using natural vents in a geologically active area can be seen in the Colline Metallifere in Tuscany.

8.3   In an area of lower enthalpy geothermal heat such as the UK, there are two main opportunities for geothermal heat (but, with lower temperatures, not electricity generation):

- Sedimentary rocks where the aquifers are deep enough to be naturally warm. There are known resources in Sherwood sandstone strata, found especially on the Yorkshire and Lincolnshire coasts but also in Hampshire, Worcestershire, Cheshire and Northern Ireland. Here, the hot water can be drawn up and should be returned to avoid any risk of subsidence. As the liquid is usually a brine it needs a corrosion resistant heat exchanger. It is also likely to contain carbon dioxide, hydrogen sulphide and other gases requiring management.

Southampton has a district heating scheme for its civic buildings, taking brine at 70°C from the underlying sandstone and there is a similar scheme in Paris. DECC is supporting three trial sites, in Newcastle, Southampton and Keele.

- "Hot dry rocks", which while not dry do not have readily available aquifers, require the exploitation of fractures in the rock. The most promising areas in the UK are the granite rocks of south west England, the Lake District, Weardale and the Grampians. Exploiting these entails significant cost in drilling deep into hard crystalline rocks in order to achieve an effective heat exchange as liquid has to be pumped down and back, using techniques from the oil industry. There will be large uncertainties about the costs of any scheme at this stage. An experimental two kilometres deep scheme at Rosemanowes in Cornwall in the 1980s required a third shaft to be drilled for it to work.

8.4   The Eden Project has planning permission to develop its own site in Cornwall with bores drilled 4.5km deep into the granite, delivering 3 – 4MW of power by 2013.

8.5   These technologies are less advanced and more expensive than those for the exploitation of active geology. RHI support for deep geothermal systems is currently available under the ground source heat pump tariff, but a deep geothermal tariff may be created in future if it seems likely that more schemes will be put forward.

SECTION C: FINANCE

9. INCOME AND SAVINGS

9.1 Income streams

9.1.1 Owners of renewable heating systems may be able to generate income streams from Government support schemes and from the sale of heat. The possible sources of income include:

- Payments under the Renewable Heat Incentive (RHI) for heat generated (see 10.0 below);
- For Combined Heat and Power (CHP) plants, payments under the Feed-in Tariff regime for electricity generated;
- Sales income for the supply of heat to other properties, particularly under district heating schemes.

9.1.2 Further indirect support is available to businesses through the capital allowances scheme (see 14.1 below).

9.2 Savings

9.2.1 When more expensive forms of heating, such as oil-fired boilers, are replaced by renewable heating systems, significant savings on property running costs can be made. These are impossible to quantify in a general way as there will be many variables for each individual property. However, savings might be smaller than expected if heating becomes affordable where it was not before and so properties which were under-heated are now consuming more heat.

9.3 Sales of heat or fuel

9.3.1 Where property owners can install a heating system which feeds multiple properties, there may be opportunities to sell heat to the occupiers. Various arrangements for such a supply are available and as this becomes a more common practice, it is likely that many variations will be designed to suit the needs of the particular parties.

9.3.2 While a rent inclusive of heat charges may appear more straightforward, it may raise VAT issues. If the heat generation is part of VAT-able business, its supply would usually create a VAT-able input (standard rated for commercial use, 5% for domestic use) to a rent which, unless the option to tax has been exercised, would be exempt. As a practical matter, this basis gives no incentive for the tenant to minimise the heat consumed.

9.3.3 If the supply of heat is to be invoiced separately, a heat meter should be installed so that readings can be taken to ensure accurate bills. With a ground source heat pump, the minimum charge might be just for the electricity used by the pumps themselves, perhaps with a margin for servicing and any return on capital. On a more commercial basis the heat might be charged for on a basis linking the heat supplied in some way to the value of oil or another alternative fuel or benefit.

9.3.4 A heat supply agreement might include the following terms:
- The responsibilities of the parties
- An undertaking to supply a specified amount of heat
- The basis of how the charges are calculated – this may be by reference to an index of alternative fuel costs, or on a cost sharing basis, for example
- How and when the charges will be reviewed

- Apportionment of charges at the end of the term
- Provision for disputes resolution
- Contingency plans in the event of a failure of the system, which might include provision of back-up boilers or temporary heating.

9.4   Sales of fuel

9.4.1   Those who are growing their own biomass feedstock might choose to sell fuel, rather than heat, to third parties. Some have entered into supply contracts which link the price of the biomass fuel to the price of heating oil. One of the largest district heating systems in the country is in Sheffield, where municipal waste is burned to produce heat and electricity. Heat is supplied to over 140 council and private sector buildings and the basis of charging is an index linking the cost of heat to the price of alternative fuels for the duration of the supply contract.

9.4.2   In addition, biomass growers may be eligible for other forms of support, such as woodland management grant schemes for those growing their own woodfuel (see 12.0 below).

9.4.3   Those making supplies of heat or fuel will, if registered, have to account for VAT, which is charged at the standard rate for businesses and at the reduced rate (currently 5%) for domestic supplies.

10. THE RENEWABLE HEAT INCENTIVE

10.1   Introduction

10.1.1   The details of the RHI are set out in the Renewable Heat Incentive Regulations 2011, which are expected to come into force on 30th September 2011.

10.1.2   The objective of the RHI is set out in the March 2011 DECC policy document 'Renewable Heat':

> *"to increase significantly the proportion of heat that is generated from renewable sources and, by encouraging a switch from fossil fuels, contribute towards our wider carbon reduction goals."*

10.1.3   The higher cost of renewable heat systems compared to fossil fuel based alternatives has been recognised as being a barrier to their wider use. The RHI is intended to compensate for this by providing payments for the heat produced by the system which should give a reasonable return on the investment. DECC expects renewable heating costs to fall over time and it is likely that the payment rates under the RHI will also fall to reflect this – an approach referred to as 'degressivity'. The Committee on Climate Change's Renewable Energy Review warns, however, that payment levels may need to be maintained for some years to ensure sufficient market penetration for these technologies, which are still relatively unknown in the UK.

10.1.4   While Feed-in Tariffs for renewable electricity production are paid for by all consumers through their electricity bills, the RHI is taxpayer funded, because there is no nationwide infrastructure to deliver heat which would allow a charge on all bills in the same way. The Government has earmarked £860 million for it in the period 2011 – 2014, expecting this to stimulate the installation of over 120,000 installations in the non-domestic sector alone, producing around 57TWh of renewable heat.

10.1.5   The RHI scheme will apply in England, Scotland and Wales and will be introduced in two phases: "non-domestic premises" – essentially any scheme larger than a single installation for a single dwelling – will be eligible for the scheme from October 2011 and single domestic properties will be able to apply from October 2012.

10.2   Phase One – "Non-Domestic" Users and Renewable Heat Premium Payments.

10.2.1   An RHI Tariff will be introduced for "non-domestic" users from October 2011, but installations completed and commissioned after 15th July 2009 which meet the criteria will be eligible for the scheme.

10.2.2   Non-domestic users include those in the commercial, industrial and public sectors, as well as not-for-profit organisations and communities. It will include schemes which provide heat to more than one dwelling, such as district heating schemes, and those where a dwelling has been "significantly adapted for non-residential use" such as bed and breakfast establishments. Dwellings where there has been no significant adaptation – such as where someone works from home – will be domestic premises and not eligible for the scheme.

10.2.3   **Renewable Heat Premium Payments** (RHPP) were introduced for domestic users on 1st August 2011. These are grants intended to assist with the capital cost of acquiring and installing renewable heat equipment in domestic property. This is a short-term scheme, running until 31st March 2012 and designed to bridge the gap before the Renewable Heat Incentive and the Green Deal come into force for domestic property in 2012.

10.2.4 The RHPP scheme operates on a first-come, first-served basis. Only those properties which do not have access to mains gas will be eligible for the following grants:

- Ground source heat pump: £1250
- Biomass boiler: £950
- Air source heat pump: £850

In addition, grants of £300 towards the cost of solar thermal hot water panels are available to all householders, whether or not they are connected to the mains gas grid.

10.2.5   The conditions of the scheme for Renewable Heat Premium Payments include:
- Basic energy efficiency measures must be in place before the new equipment is installed, which means a minimum of 250 mm of loft insulation plus cavity wall insulation where practical. It will be advisable to check the current level of insulation in a property at the earliest opportunity.
- Participants will be required to contribute to two surveys designed to assess the efficiency and output of the heaters. In a random sample, additional heat meters will be fitted to the equipment to monitor its performance in more detail.
- The equipment and the installer must be certified under the Microgeneration Certification Scheme.
- The house where the equipment is installed must be the main home of the applicant. This implies that second homes will not be able to benefit from the scheme.
- Tenants who wish to purchase energy saving equipment themselves can apply, but must have their landlord's permission. Landlords may be eligible for payments under the Renewable Heat Incentive (from October for non-domestic or multiple properties; from 2012 for single domestic dwellings) where they will install and pay for the equipment.

10.2.6 The Energy Saving Trust will administer the RHPP scheme and more information is available from its website.

10.3   Phase Two – Domestic Users.
10.3.1   A domestic RHI Tariff is to be introduced from October 2012. The 'Green Deal' for homes is also to start then, supporting an emphasis on addressing insulation and energy saving technologies, as well as renewable heat, as part of a unified package. "Domestic unit" means a single renewable heat installation serving one dwelling house, so for example if a landlord wishes to install individual biomass boilers in several houses, each installation will qualify as a domestic unit. If the landlord installs a district heating system with a single boiler heating several houses, that would be a non-domestic installation which would qualify for the RHI in phase 1.

10.3.2   Any eligible renewable heat system completed and commissioned after 15th July 2009 will be able to apply for the RHI payments once the scheme starts in 2012.

10.4   The Payments
10.4.1   Payments under the RHI are calculated by multiplying the appropriate tariff by the actual metered heat use. It is actual heat use, rather that the rated capacity of the installation, which is critical. Claimants will lock-in to a tariff rate when their units are commissioned and this rate will then be paid for the 20 years of the scheme, adjusted for inflation annually by reference to the Retail Price Index (not the Consumer Prices Index, now the Government's preferred measure of inflation, which has historically been lower than RPI).

10.4.2 Payments have been set at a level which should give a rate of return close to 12%, except for the payments for solar thermal, which, because it is the most expensive of the technologies, have been set to give a lower rate of return. The rates themselves will be reviewed annually but are expected to fall for future scheme years in line with an expected fall in the cost of the technology.

10.4.3 The figures set out below are those in the 2011 Regulations. These will be periodically reviewed during the life of the scheme.

Table 1: RHI Tariffs for industry, business and large organisations

Tariff name	Eligible technology	Eligible sizes	Tariff rate (pence/ kWh)	Tariff duration (Years)	Support calculation
Small commercial biomass	Solid biomass including solid biomass contained in municipal solid waste and CHP	Less than 200kW$_{th}$	Tier 1: **7.9** Tier 2: **2.0**	20	Metering. Tier 1 applies annually up to the Tier Break, Tier 2 above it. The Tier Break is: installed capacity x 1,314 peak load hours, i.e.: kW$_{th}$ **x 1,314**
Medium commercial biomass		200kW$_{th}$ and above up to but not including 1MW$_{th}$	Tier 1: **4.9** Tier 2: **2.0**		
Large commercial biomass		1MW$_{th}$ and above	**2.7**		Metering
Small commercial heat pumps	Ground-source and water-source heat pump; deep geothermal	Less than 100kW$_{th}$	**4.5**	20	Metering
Large commercial heat pumps		100kW$_{th}$ and above	**3.2**		
All solar collectors	Solar collectors	Below 200kW$_{th}$	**8.5**	20	Metering
Biomethane and biogas combustion	Biomethane injection and biogas combustion	All biomethane injection and biogas combustion below 200kW$_{th}$	**6.8**	20	Metering

10.4.4   Installations which have been awarded grant funding from other sources will not be eligible for the RHI.

10.4.5   Unlike Feed-in Tariffs, there is no maximum threshold for the RHI, except for solar thermal and biogas projects, both of which must have a capacity of less than $200kW_{th}$.

10.4.6   Tiering applies to the small and medium scale biomass tariffs as part of the efforts to avoid incentives to generate excess heat in order to maximise payments. A higher payment rate is available for the first 1,314 hours of output, which equates to the plant operating at full capacity for 15% of the year. Any additional heat generated above this figure is paid at a lower rate.

10.4.7   Those who require a system with an output close to the thresholds will see the benefit in installing a slightly smaller boiler. For example, a 190kW boiler operating for 2,200 hours per year would produce about the same amount of heat as a 210kW boiler operating for 1,990 hours, but significantly different RHI payments:

190kW boiler x 1,314 hrs =	249,660kWh @ 7.9p =	£19,723.14
190kW boiler x 886 hrs =	168,340kWh @ 2.0p =	£3,366.80
Total =	418,000kWh	£23,089.94
210kW boiler x 1,314 hrs =	275,940kWh @ 4.9p =	£13,521.06
210kW boiler x 676 hrs =	141,960kWh @ 2.0p =	£2,839.20
Total =	417,900kWh	£16,360.26

10.4.8   It should be noted that there will be other practical factors to consider when selecting a boiler, such as whether extra thermal storage tanks would be needed with a smaller boiler, which might add to the overall cost.

10.5   Eligible Installations
10.5.1   An installation will be eligible if it meets the requirements set out in the Regulations as to the technology type, the date of commissioning, the heating method, the scale, the measurement of heat and the heating use.

10.5.2   The eligible technologies are those which:
- are purpose designed and built to generate heat from solid biomass only;
- generate heat from solid biomass contained in municipal waste;
- generate heat using a solar collector, defined as "a liquid filled flat plate or evacuated tube solar collector", provided that the installation capacity is less than $200kW_{th}$;
- are heat pumps generating heat using naturally occurring energy from the ground (other than geothermal) or from surface water, provided that the installation has a coefficient of performance of at least 2.9;
- are combined heat and power (CHP) systems generating heat from solid biomass, biogas, or deep geothermal (naturally occurring heat from at least 500m below the surface of the earth);
- generate heat from naturally occurring sources at least 500m beneath the surface of the earth (deep geothermal heat systems);
- generate heat using biogas from AD, gasification or pyrolysis, provided that the installation capacity is less than $200kW_{th}$ and provided that the heat is not generated from solid biomass.

10.5.3   For any of the above technologies to be eligible, the plant must have been new at the time of commission and completed and first commissioned on or after 15th July 2009 (the date when the Renewable Energy Strategy was published). A plant first commissioned as a CHP plant on or after 15th July 2009 will be deemed to be a new plant for this purpose, thus recently installed schemes may qualify. Any grants already received for such schemes would have to be repaid in order for them to be able to receive RHI payments (see 10.7 below).

10.5.4   Eligible plants must use liquid or steam as a medium for delivering heat to the space, water or process which is to be heated and the heat must be used in a building or other enclosed structure in order to be an "eligible use". Process heating is permitted and could include, for example, running a grain dryer.

10.5.5   The scheme will not include air source heat pumps from the start, although further work is to be done to see whether they should be included in future. Other non-eligible technologies include:
  • direct air heating;
  • combustion of bio-liquids;
  • co-firing biomass with fossil fuel;
  • exhaust air heat pumps;
  • transpired solar thermal;
  • fossil fuel fired CHP;
  • waste heat from fossil fuel.

10.6   Eligibility for Payments
10.6.1   The RHI Tariff will operate in a similar way to the Feed-in Tariff. Payments will be made quarterly for each kilowatt hour of heat (kWhth) produced from an accredited installation. Installations will have to be fitted with heat meters to allow heat production to be measured; in the case of standard equipment such as biomass boilers, the capacity of the system should be verifiable by the manufacturer. Bespoke systems will need to be able to prove their capacity to Ofgem.

10.6.2   Smaller capacity systems receive higher payment rates to reflect the additional costs involved. Measures have been put in place to ensure that there is no incentive for applicants to seek to install multiple smaller units when a single larger system would be appropriate:
  – where multiple units are installed within 12 months, the additional capacity will be treated as if it were part of the original installation and the tariff for all the units will be calculated on the total combined capacity of all of the units at the rate in place when the first unit was commissioned;
  – where additional capacity is added more than 12 months later, Ofgem can review the accreditation of the original plant and take enforcement action if any ongoing obligations are not being complied with;
  – additional capacity must be individually metered.

10.6.3   Only heat sources which are defined as "renewable" in the Renewable Energy Directive will be eligible for the payments. There are restrictions on the proportion of fossil fuels which are permitted within solid biomass from municipal waste.

10.6.4   Only "useful heat" will be eligible for payments. This term will not be precisely defined, but the principles are set out in the DECC policy document and include reference to supplying economically justifiable heat requirements and not artificially created or enhanced ones.

10.6.5 Only the "owner" of the RHI scheme will receive the payments. "Owner" will have its standard meaning, so that it will usually be the person (or people, or company) who has exclusive rights and liabilities in respect of the installation. The RHI will not be assignable, unlike the Feed-in Tariff.

10.7   RHI and other grants
10.7.1   As with most public grants, the basic principle is that there should be no double funding of any project. Therefore any scheme which has received grants from another source to fund the installation of renewable heat equipment (including local authorities, regional funds or EU schemes such as the RDPE) will not be eligible for the RHI. Schemes which were commissioned after 15th July 2009 and which received grants before the RHI Regulations came into force can become eligible for the RHI if they repay those grants. If a project receives grant funding after the date when the RHI Regulations came into force they will not be eligible for the RHI. Further details are awaited as it may be that a *de minimis* limit will apply to grant funding already received, as it does in the FiT scheme.

10.7.2   Grants for other, related activities may be able to be claimed alongside the RHI, such as the Energy Crops Scheme which offer grants to support the establishment of short rotation coppice and miscanthus in England. (See 12.0 for further detail.)

10.8   RHI and the Renewables Obligation and Feed-in Tariffs
10.8.1   The Renewables Obligation (RO) currently provides support for combined heat and power (CHP) schemes. Those projects which currently receive RO support will not be eligible for the RHI. However, the Government intend to review this arrangement at the next review of ROC banding, which is due to take effect in 2013.

10.8.2   Feed-in Tariffs (FiTs) only provide support for electricity generation and therefore it will be possible for CHP units which are already receiving FiTs for electricity to receive RHI support for the heat generation part of the project.

10.9   Accreditation
10.9.1   The scheme will be accredited and administered by Ofgem. Owners of eligible installations should apply in writing to Ofgem with full details of the proposals; Schedule 1 of the RHI Regulations sets out the information required and this is reproduced in Appendix VI. Ofgem may accredit a plant with or without conditions, or refuse accreditation, in which case it must give reasons. Notification of accreditation must be in writing and must include:
  • The date of accreditation
  • The applicable tariff
  • The process and timing for providing meter readings
  • Details of the frequency and timetable for payments
  • The tariff lifetime and end date.

10.9.2   Accreditation for larger installations can be a two tier process so that applicants can apply for 'initial accreditation' by submitting plans and details of a proposed scheme to Ofgem. If the proposals meet the scheme criteria, Ofgem will award initial accreditation to it and provided that the scheme is built in accordance with the plans (or any agreed changes) then Ofgem will accredit the completed project. This is designed to give confidence to investors and lenders that capital-intensive projects will be eligible for the RHI on completion. Initial accreditation is not available for solar collectors; ground or water source heat pumps; or sold biomass plants with a capacity of less than $200kW_{th}$.

10.9.3 Changes in ownership will need to be notified to Ofgem within 12 months, with appropriate supporting evidence, in order for the remaining RHI payments to be transferred to the new owner.

10.10 Ongoing obligations

The Regulations set out (at Regulation 34) 'ongoing obligations' with which all participants in the RHI scheme must comply. These include an obligation not to generate heat for the predominant purpose of increasing the RHI payments. Other obligations include:

- Keeping records of fuel used and purchased
- Keeping service and maintenance records
- Providing evidence, if requested, that the heat generated is used for an eligible purpose
- Notifying Ofgem within 28 days of
    - any change in ownership
    - the addition or removal of any part of the installation
    - ceasing to comply with an obligation or becoming aware of anything affecting eligibility to claim the payments.

10.11 Microgeneration

Small scale biomass boilers, solar thermal systems or heat pumps of $45kW_{th}$ capacity or less must have both plant and installer certified by the Microgeneration Certification Scheme.

10.12 Heat meters

10.12.1 All renewable heat installations must include a heat meter to record the heat actually produced if they are to be eligible for the RHI. It must meet the Class 2 requirements listed in Annex MI-004 of the EU Measuring Instruments Directive 2004. All meters must be correctly calibrated and properly installed.

10.12.2 If more than one type of installation is in place at the same location (for example, a biomass boiler and a ground source heat pump) then each must be fitted with an individual meter. Shared meters are only permitted where the different installations use the same fuel, are eligible for the same tariff and will have the same tariff start date and end date.

10.12.3 Plants using steam to transfer heat must use steam measuring equipment and a heat meter to measure any condensate returned to the system.

10.12.4 Heat meter readings must be submitted to Ofgem. There will not be a facility to submit readings automatically at the start of the scheme, although DECC are investigating whether this might be possible in future.

10.13 Reviews

The first review of the RHI is proposed to take effect in 2015, but DECC has reserved the right to carry out an earlier review if there is 'any significant change to the assumptions which underpin the RHI'. An early review of FiT rates for solar pv projects halted many large developments in their tracks.

10.14 Compliance and Enforcement

Applicants will have to certify that they meet the rules of the RHI scheme on application and they will need to submit an annual declaration confirming that they continue to comply. Failure to comply with the rules of the scheme could result in any of a range of sanctions being applied, including:

- Compliance notice
- Temporary or permanent withholding of payments
- Reduction of future payments
- Exclusion from the scheme
- Prosecution.

10.15   Thresholds for schemes

10.15.1 Aside from any practical limits imposed by energy sources, economies of scale, the property or available finance, the framework of public support creates a number of thresholds for the production capacity of schemes. The most obvious ones across most technologies are:

- $45kW_{th}$ – the level at or below which biomass, ground and water source heat pumps and solar thermal plants must be certified under the Microgeneration Certification Scheme or equivalent to be eligible for the RHI.
- $100kW_{th}$ – the ceiling below which a ground source heat pump scheme is defined as 'small' in the RHI, thereby qualifying for the higher tariff rate.
- $200kW_{th}$ – the ceiling for solar thermal and biogas combustion plants to qualify for the RHI; also the level below which biomass projects are defined as 'small' for the RHI, thereby qualifying for the highest tariff rate (see example above at 10.4.7).
- $1,000kW_{th}$ – the level at or above which biomass projects are defined as 'large' for the RHI, thereby qualifying for the lowest tariff rate.

10.15.2 The higher rates of payments under the RHI for the smaller schemes do not necessarily make them more attractive but will generally be to compensate for loss of economies of scale. Nonetheless, with the scale of payments currently on offer, these tiers may affect the design size of a scheme, given other constraints.

10.15.3 There are safeguards to prevent one owner claiming for multiple smaller systems where one larger system would be appropriate: where multiple units are installed within 12 months, the tariff for all the units will be calculated on the total combined capacity of all of the units at the rate in place when the first unit was commissioned. Where additional capacity is added more than 12 months later, the tariff on the original part of the scheme will be unaffected, but the tariff payment on the new capacity will be calculated on the basis of the combined capacity of all the units, at the payment rate in place when the new unit is commissioned.

11. THE GREEN DEAL

11.1   The Green Deal is a method of funding energy efficiency measures for property by linking the repayments for the improvement works to the property's energy bills, so that the customer does not have to pay in advance for improvements which should save money over many years to come. Both domestic and commercial properties will be eligible for the Green Deal, which is expected to be delivered by a range of private sector businesses, such as energy companies, home improvement stores, local authorities and housing associations, who will be referred to as 'Green Deal Providers'.

11.2   The statutory framework for the Green Deal is set out in the Energy Bill, which will be followed by Regulations covering the detail of its implementation. It is due to be available to customers from 2012.

11.3   The Green Deal process will start when a customer contacts a Green Deal Provider to request a Green Deal Plan. The Plan will be prepared by an accredited adviser who will inspect the property and suggest measures which could be taken to improve energy efficiency. The suggested measures must be from an approved list and the criteria by which those measures are assessed will be set out in the Regulations.

11.4   The Plan must comply with the so-called 'Golden Rule': the total cost of installing the energy saving measures (including finance costs) must not exceed the expected financial savings which the customer should make.

11.5   The Provider may then choose to make an offer to the customer setting out:
• the measures to be undertaken,
• the total cost,
• the charge to be added to the energy bill, and
• the length of the repayment period.

11.6   Only those measures which are approved and recommended by an accredited adviser can be included in the Plan and only if they are also fitted by an accredited installer will they be eligible for the Green Deal. Customers will be able to choose their Green Energy Provider and should exercise caution in doing so; it remains to be seen whether there could be conflicts of interest if, for example, a home improvement business is recommending the installation of products which it will then supply.

11.7   Before a customer can accept the offer, they must obtain the consent of the energy bill payer and all those with an interest in the property. As well as landlords, tenants and occupiers, this might also include the mortgagee, the mortgagor, beneficiaries of trusts and remaindermen. Once the Plan and offer are accepted, the Provider will arrange for the work to be carried out by accredited installers.

11.8   The existence of a Green Deal Plan must be disclosed to anyone who takes on responsibility for paying the energy bills for the property. It is expected that this will be linked to the requirement to produce an Energy Performance Certificate when a property is sold or let, but the final details – to be included in the Regulations – are not yet available. Other questions arise when considering what happens if a property is vacant for an extended period of time, or where it is redeveloped. The potential impact on the future energy bill payer will need to be taken into account, but how this will be dealt with is not yet clear from the information released by the Government so far.

11.9   The customer can choose to pay for the works in advance in an ordinary commercial transaction, but the main feature of the Green Deal is that the improvements can be funded by a charge added to the energy bill so that there is no upfront cost to the owner or occupier. The confirmed Green Deal charge is added to the energy bill which is paid as usual by the owner or occupier to the energy supplier. The energy supplier undertakes to pass the Green Deal charge from the energy bill back to the Green Deal Provider. If a customer defaults on their Green Deal payment, the energy supplier can seek to recover it in the same way as any other outstanding bill, including having the option of cutting off the energy supply.

11.10   In order to manage this financial arrangement, the Green Deal Provider will need to hold a Consumer Credit Licence from the Office of Fair Trading. Energy suppliers will be exempt from this requirement as they are already regulated and licensed by Ofgem.

11.11   Customers will be able to elect to pay back the Green Deal amount early, either in full or in part, but Providers will be able to levy early repayment charges to cover any losses they would incur as a result, provided that those charges are fair and justifiable.

11.12   Aware that the Golden Rule (see 11.4 above) means that the Green Deal will not be available to all those who might benefit from it, the Government also proposes to introduce a new Energy Companies Obligation (ECO) which will be aimed at lower income households and at property types which are more difficult to upgrade, such as those of solid wall construction. The ECO will replace existing obligations on energy companies (the Carbon Emissions Reduction Target and the Community Energy Saving Programme) when they end in December 2012. The ECO programme will be integrated into the Green Deal so that customers do not have to make multiple applications. More detail on the ECO programme is expected to be available later in 2011.

11.13   The Green Deal will have a cap of £10,000 worth of expenditure per property, but the constraint of the Golden Rule suggests that few will qualify for anything close to that figure. For example, to achieve proposed savings of, say, £200 per year, the repayment cost of the improvements must be less than that – about £17 per month. Over 10 years at 6%, this would repay a capital sum of about £1,500; over 20 years at 6% it could repay £2,340. As illustrations, this suggests that in many cases, the works may have to be fairly modest.

11.14   Figures published by DECC propose that cavity wall insulation costing around £500 can result in savings of up to £115 per year for an average three-bedroom, semi-detached house, but this is based on a property with gas fired central heating. Given that running costs for oil fired heating systems (more common in rural areas) are about double those of gas, the savings might be expected to be greater and the payback period shorter where the property is oil-fired.

11.15   Retro-fitting insulation in older properties
It should be noted that retro-fitting insulation in older properties can be very problematic, as they were often designed to 'breathe', with plenty of ventilation through chimney stacks, airbricks and single-glazed windows. Modern efforts to reduce draughts, block chimneys and install double glazing will reduce natural ventilation and can exacerbate damp problems. For example, installing insulation into older cavity walls is far from straightforward, as the cavity was designed to provide a layer of air as insulation with a minimal risk that damp could breach it. Poorly installed cavity wall

insulation can cause long-term problems with damp and professional advice should always be sought from a suitably qualified and independent practitioner as to the appropriate materials and method for a particular property. The insulation of solid walls can be just as difficult. Internal insulation will reduce the size of rooms and is disruptive to fit, as window and door frames and skirting boards will all have to be removed and re-fitted. Externally applied insulation, which is often more expensive and changes the appearance of buildings which are not already rendered, can also affect the building's ability to 'breathe'. In either case, there may be additional problems for listed buildings.

12. OTHER GRANT SCHEMES

12.1   Introduction

Grants which would double-fund the installation of renewable heat technology are not eligible if the RHI is being claimed, but some grant schemes offer funding for related upstream or downstream activities, including:

12.2   England

12.2.1   The Forestry Commission's Woodfuel Strategy for England and Implementation Plan sets out how they are encouraging the market for logs, woodchip and pellets to develop.

12.2.2   The Woodland Grant Scheme supports the planting and management of woodlands for a variety of uses.

12.2.3   The Energy Crops Scheme, administered by Natural England, will fund up to 50% of the establishment costs for short rotation coppice and miscanthus. Further detail can be found on the Natural England website (www.naturalengland.org.uk).

12.2.4   Rural Development Programme for England (RDPE) funding may still be available in some areas, although budgets are under pressure.

12.2.5   The Energyshare fund makes grants to community groups across Britain of up to £100,000, for community projects that have the objective of saving or generating energy locally.

12.3   Wales

12.3.1   A new Glastir Woodland Creation Grant has in part replaced the Better Woodlands for Wales scheme, which has now closed.

12.3.2   Forestry Commission Wales runs the Wood Energy Business Scheme, which provides funding to small businesses (but not farms) and community groups across Wales which are installing wood fuelled heating systems.

12.3.3   Forestry Commission Wales supports the Woodfuel Wales website (www.woodfuelwales.org.uk) which provides information to users and suppliers of woodfuel.

12.4   Scotland

12.4.1   Forestry Commission Scotland leads the Woodfuel Task Force to support the development of a woodfuel supply chain in Scotland and supports the Use Woodfuel website (www.usewoodfuel.co.uk) which provides information to both consumers and producers.

12.4.2   Woodland grants are available under the Scottish Rural Development Programme for woodland creation and management and to help small businesses to invest in renewable technology or set up supply chains.

12.4.3   The Communities and Renewable Energy Scheme (CARES) is offering loan funds of up to £150,000 covering up to 90% of the costs of establishing locally owned renewable energy projects which offer wider community benefits and where there is a partnership with the local community.

12.5   Closed schemes – A series of schemes which had been supporting some renewable heat projects have been closed in anticipation of the RHI funding stream. These include:

- Low Carbon Buildings Programme
- Bio-energy Infrastructure Scheme
- Bio-energy Capital Grants Scheme
- Scottish Biomass Heat Support Scheme
- Better Woodlands for Wales.

13. THE GREEN INVESTMENT BANK

13.1   The Green Investment Bank is expected to be operational by April 2012, although it will not have borrowing powers until April 2015. With an initial £3 billion of capital (to be funded by asset sales but underwritten by the Treasury), it is likely to start by investing in sectors such as offshore wind, energy efficiency and waste with the intention that it will mitigate some of the risk associated with the green economy and make such investments more attractive to commercial funds and institutions. The Bank might also be involved in delivering the first stages of the Green Deal, although how it would do so has not been set out.

13.2   The Coalition Government intends that the Bank will have operational independence, once State Aid rules are satisfied, with the aim that it will then expand beyond straight investment into other financial services, eventually getting borrowing powers in April 2015. The Government predicts that the initial £3 billion capital will be able to stimulate total investment of around £15 billion, although it gives no timescale for this aim.

13.3   Further detail on the scope and structure of the Green Investment Bank will emerge when the draft legislation to bring it into being is published, but it may be several years before the effects of its investments are felt in the green economy.

14. TAXATION MATTERS

Note – Taxation matters, as they stood in early 2011, are covered in greater detail in Chapter 18 of On-Farm Generation of Renewable Electricity. Since then, adverse changes have been made to both Capital Allowances and the Enterprise Investment Scheme (EIS).

14.1 Capital Allowances

14.1.1 In May 2011 Her Majesty's Revenue and Customs (HMRC) launched a consultation on the future of capital allowances for plant and machinery used to claim Feed-in Tariffs (FiTs) or payments under the Renewable Heat Incentive (RHI). The aim of the consultation is to consider proposed legislation which will "*clarify the appropriate capital allowances treatment of expenditure on plant or machinery that could qualify for payments under either the Feed-in Tariff regime or the Renewable Heat Incentive*".

14.1.2 **Current situation** – Businesses that invest in plant and machinery used to generate electricity or heat from renewable sources can claim the usual capital allowances, even if they are claiming FiT payments or plan to claim payments under the RHI:

- The Annual Investment Allowance – a 100% allowance on the first £100,000 of expenditure. The limit is to be reduced to £25,000 from April 2012.

- Writing Down Allowances at a rate of 20% (18% from April 2012) or 10% (8% from April 2012) for any unrelieved expenditure. The lower rate applies to "special rate expenditure" and the categories to which this applies are set out in the Finance Act 2008, including long-life assets and those assets which are integral features of a building. HMRC states that there is some doubt as to whether the lower rate would apply to plant and machinery used for renewable energy.

14.1.3 In addition, Enhanced Capital Allowances (ECAs) may be available in some cases. ECAs are 100% first year allowances for energy saving equipment, which allows the full capital cost of the equipment to be offset against taxable profits made in the same period. Qualifying plant and machinery is that which is included on the Energy Technology Criteria List which is approved by the DECC and HMRC. The criteria for the list are reviewed annually and the list of qualifying products is updated every month. At the time of writing, the technology list includes biomass boilers, ground and water source heat pumps, solar collectors and products used in combined heat and power systems. Full details can be found on the dedicated website www.eca.gov.uk.

14.1.4 **Proposals** – In the consultation document, the Government takes the view that the payments made under FiTs and the RHI are designed to provide a return on investment and it is not, therefore, either necessary or appropriate to give further incentives in the form of generous capital allowances. If this is implemented, ECAs would not be available for renewable energy plant and machinery and Writing Down Allowances would only be available at the lower rate.

14.1.5 The consultation is due to close on 31st August 2011 and the intention is that draft legislation would be set out by the end of 2011. It is likely that any changes would come into effect from April 2012.

14.1.6   While it can be argued that where capital allowances are available, their rate is largely about the timing of tax relief, these changes may adversely affect the cash flow consequences of some proposals. In the longer term, they create a growing mismatch between depreciation and the allowances that substitute for it in tax accounts, effectively imposing a higher rate of tax on capital intensive projects.

14.2   Enterprise Investment Schemes

The Enterprise Investment Scheme (EIS) offers income and capital gains tax reliefs to investors who purchase new shares in smaller, higher-risk trading companies, thus enabling them to raise finance. Farming and landownership are not eligible for EIS, but the scheme may provide opportunities for tax efficient investment into new renewable energy ventures. The tax reliefs available were extended in the Finance Act 2011 to make the scheme more attractive to investors and encourage more direct investment into smaller companies. However, the Government has announced that it plans to introduce measures in the 2012 Finance Bill to make the receipt of Feed-in Tariffs or similar subsidies an "excluded activity" so that companies whose trade consisted wholly or primarily of receipt of such subsidies would not be eligible for EIS. This measure would not apply to shares issued before 23rd March 2011, or where the company commences electricity generation before 6th April 2012. It seems likely that the exclusion would also apply to RHI payments.

14.3   Stamp Duty Land Tax Relief for Zero-Carbon Homes

From 1 October 2007, no stamp duty land tax (SDLT) is payable on the first purchase of a zero-carbon home up to a purchase price of £500,000. Where the purchase price is in excess of £500,000, then the SDLT liability will be reduced by £15,000 and the balance of the tax will be due in the normal way.

SECTION D: PRACTICALITIES

15. DESIGNING A RENEWABLE HEAT SYSTEM

15.1   Introduction

Introducing an entirely new heating system to an existing property or a development requires careful planning and preparation. It is often the case that it may be cheaper to do this as part of an entirely new development rather than adapting an existing structure ("retro-fitting"), yet most work will involve that adaptation. Some of the questions to be considered are set out below and a checklist of others can be found at the start of this publication.

15.2   What can be done to improve the efficiency of current systems?

Investing in a new heating system is only part of an answer and there may be little point in spending large sums of money if the heat will escape from poorly insulated or managed buildings. Renovation or conversion projects offer the opportunity to consider the insulation of floors and walls as well as roof voids. One very large country house found that significant savings could be made by running the existing heating system continuously, but at lower temperatures, instead of turning it on and off several times a day. An audit of current heat use and property condition is a useful starting point.

15.3   What is to be heated?

15.3.1 How many buildings are included in the plan? What is their current and proposed future use? If there are mixed domestic and commercial uses which will be occupied at different times of the day, then the heating system will need to provide a more or less constant flow, at least during the winter. It may be necessary to have a back-up system based on an oil or gas fired boiler; commercial and residential tenants paying rent will expect a constant and reliable heating system, as will guests in bed and breakfast establishments or holiday cottages.

15.3.2 As it may be expensive to extend or enlarge a scheme at a later date, potential future development should be planned for as far as possible in practical terms and within the budget. A system designed for current requirements may be insufficient to cope with extra demand should farm buildings be converted to offices, for example. If additional demand is likely, it may be worth designing a system to which additional capacity can be added at a later date if needed, rather than facing the additional cost of building in over-capacity from the start.

15.3.3 What is the current heating system in use? Can any of its infrastructure, such as pipes and radiators, be used in the new system? Some heating systems will connect to existing circuits relatively easily; but for example, ground and water source heat pumps are often used with an underfloor heating system, which is difficult to install into an existing building unless the property is subject to a substantial overhaul.

15.4   What will the heat source be?

Will the heat source be reliable? The answer to this might be established through measurement of likely solar radiation for solar thermal systems, or assessing the suitability of the geology for deep thermal heat, or considering a supply chain for fuel for a biomass boiler. It will be important to consider the future supply of the heat source and what factors might influence its cost. Biomass systems will need secure supply chains and the processing, storage and handling requirements of the fuel will need to be considered. The most reliable heat source will be one over which the property owner has control – such as wood from owned woodlands. Where feedstock has to be bought in, the system is vulnerable to market developments, such as potential shortages in the supply of wood pellets or chip.

15.5   What technology is needed?

15.5.1   The heat demand will need to be assessed in order to establish the capacity of the proposed system. This will steer the decision as to the most appropriate system and technology. Some technology, such as the biomass boiler, is familiar and the expertise to install and maintain it will be widely available. This might not be the case in the UK for what is, to us, fairly new technology, such as a deep geothermal system or solar thermal units – so far seen only at a domestic level in the UK. If expertise and spare parts are not readily available in the locality, then contingency arrangements will need to be in place should the system fail. Generally, the less established the technology, the more doubts there must be about its efficiency and reliability.

15.5.2   If the RHI payments are to be claimed then heat meters will need to be installed. They will also be necessary in district heating systems where occupiers are to pay for the heat supplied.

15.6   Logistics

15.6.1   Where will the heat source be situated? Conversion of an existing building to provide housing for a boiler or heat exchanger is one option and might be preferred around listed buildings. Where there is no existing building, a new structure might require planning permission, although permitted development rights might assist in some cases (see 16.1). Good access to the buildings will be needed for maintenance and for re-fuelling biomass boilers.

15.6.2   The impact on existing buildings needs to be considered. It may be that siting an AD plant too near a valuable farmhouse might not only detract from its amenity but also reduce its value for sale or security.

15.6.3   The heat source might be some distance from the end user, in which case insulated pipes will deliver the heat. These might have to be laid across existing yards, drives, gardens or grounds, passing over or under water and sewerage pipes, electricity and telecommunications cables and ducts. The route of such new pipes should be carefully planned to avoid obstructions and to minimise changes in direction, as joints and connections are often the most expensive element of the pipework.

15.7   Regulation and consents

15.7.1   Where the proposed system interacts with a mains water supply or electricity network, it may be necessary to secure consents for connections. Where a water heating system connects to the mains to allow it to be topped-up, the water company will require that a one-way valve be fitted to the mains supply to prevent water feeding back into the main. This will need to be inspected and then tested annually with the results submitted to the water company.

15.7.2   The detailed questions to be asked in respect of the different types of technology are considered in Section B.

15.8   Sustainability

15.8.1   Issues of sustainability are a concern to policy makers, particularly with regard to biomass crops, energy crops for AD and the use of waste as a fuel.

15.8.2   Sustainability reporting is mandatory for all installations of over $1MW_{th}$ which burn biomass and all producers of biomethane. They will have to report quarterly on the sustainability of their biomass feedstock. Smaller installations are currently exempt from the requirement but it is possible that the threshold could be lowered in future. There will be a consultation on mandatory sustainability criteria for biomass in 2012, with any changes taking effect the following year.

15.8.3   Concerns about the use of farmland to grow energy crops for AD plants were raised in the Renewable Heat Incentive policy paper and the consultation on changes to Feed-in Tariffs for small scale AD, both of spring 2011. The policy paper states that it is not Government policy to encourage energy crops based AD at the expense of using the land to grow food and indicates that the matter will be kept under review. It suggests that measures could be introduced to limit or reduce the area of land used to grow energy crops if this is perceived to become an issue, without specifying what form those measures might take.

15.8.4   DEFRA is currently carrying out a review of waste policy in England, with the aim of working towards a "zero-waste" economy. The initial findings of the review were expected in Spring 2011 but have yet to be announced.

15.8.5   Owners of under-managed woodlands who wish to bring them back into production for biomass might find that current and future wildlife and other conservation or resource management policies restrict their management options, particularly if seeking woodland grants from the Forestry Commission to off-set the costs.

15.9   Combined Heat and Power plants
15.9.1   Combined heat and power (CHP) plants will generate both electricity and heat, but the name refers to the output of the plant only and the feedstock can be anything from biomass to fossil fuel. CHP units are much more efficient than those which produce only electricity, with energy conversion efficiencies of over 75%, as opposed to 25 – 30%, because they can use the heat which would other be a wasted by-product of electricity generation.

15.9.2   The Renewables Obligation (RO) provides financial support to both the heat and electricity output of CHP plants fuelled by renewable feedstock. Alternatively, for plants of less than 5MW, it is possible to claim Feed-in Tariffs on the electricity produced and RHI payments for the heat output. The whole question of support for CHP plants will be reviewed when the Banding Review of Renewables Obligation Certificates (ROCs) takes place; this is expected in 2011 with any changes taking effect in 2013. More detailed information on the Renewables Obligation can be found in CAAV Numbered Publication 203 – The On-Farm Generation of Renewable Electricity.

16. PLANNING AND OTHER CONSENTS

16.1 Planning consents

16.1.1 A detailed review of the planning policies affecting renewable energy developments was included in CAAV Numbered Publication 203 – The On-Farm Generation of Renewable Electricity (March 2011).

16.1.2 The principal planning policy covering renewable energy in England is PPS 22 and in Wales, TAN 8. In Scotland the policy statements are set out in the Scottish Planning Policy, which supports "all scales of development" for renewable energy, with further advice on specific sectors available from the Scottish Government website.

16.1.3 Permitted development rights apply for the installation of certain microgeneration renewable energy structures to domestic property, including ground source heat pumps and flues for biomass boilers. The Regulations for England, Scotland and Wales are reproduced at Appendix 3 of Numbered Publication 203.

16.1.4 Similar provisions are made for non-residential property in Scotland by the Town and Country Planning (General Permitted Development) (Non-Domestic Microgeneration) (Scotland) Amendment Order 2011. It is expected that similar provisions will be made in England and Wales, but although a consultation on the subject closed in February 2010, there is no current indication as to when this might happen.

16.1.5 Some local authorities have introduced what is known as the Merton Rule, after the London borough which first introduced it in 2003. This requires developers to undertake to include renewable energy systems which will provide a specified proportion (often 10%) of the predicted energy needs of the development. It has been applied to both residential and non-residential developments, subject to minimum thresholds of scale.

16.2 Environmental consents

16.2.1 **Ground source heat pumps** – Closed loop heat pump systems do not require specific environmental consents.

16.2.2 Open loop ground source heat pumps, which abstract water and circulate it through a heat pump, do however require environmental consents relating to the abstraction and discharge of water.

16.2.3 In England and Wales, the Environment Agency will require a Groundwater Investigation Consent, an abstraction licence and an environmental permit to discharge the water back into the source. Its 'Environmental good practice guide for ground source heating and cooling' can be downloaded from the Environment Agency website (www.environment-agency.gov.uk) and recommends that developers of proposed systems contact them at an early stage to discuss the potential environmental impact of the scheme.

16.2.4 In Scotland, SEPA has similar requirements and in February 2010 issued 'Supporting Guidance WAT-SG-62 Groundwater Abstractions – Geothermal Energy' which can be downloaded from the SEPA website (www.sepa.org.uk).

16.2.5 **Biomass** – In England and Wales, environmental permits are required only for very large scale biomass schemes of over 50MW, or over 3MW where the biomass is classified as waste. Scotland has its own provisions.

16.2.6 **Anaerobic Digestion** – The Environmental Permitting regime applies to anaerobic digesters in England and Wales and its requirements are considered in detail in Numbered Publication 203. Scotland has its own provisions.

16.3   Part L of the Building Regulations
Part L sets out the requirements for the conservation of fuel and power when building works are carried out. It is in four parts, covering both new and existing, domestic and non-domestic buildings.

16.4   Clean Air Act 2003
If a property is situated within a Smoke Control Area under the Clean Air Act 2003 then biomass can only be burnt in an 'exempt appliance' in accordance with the conditions set out in the list maintained on the DEFRA website. (See paragraph 4.3.6.)

16.5   Waste Incineration Directive
The Environment Agency is responsible for administering the Waste Incineration Directive, which applies where any waste is burned at the rate of more than one tonne per hour. Sites burning less than this will be regulated by their local authority. The WID is likely to apply to some renewable heat schemes, such as those which burn chicken manure. The Environment Agency will, if satisfied with the proposals, issue a permit, monitor emissions and periodically inspect the plant.

17. LANDLORD AND TENANT ISSUES

17.1   Introduction

17.1.1   Where renewable heating systems are planned for let property, whether it be residential, commercial or agricultural, there are circumstances when either the landlord or the tenant might wish to carry out the work. In general, it may often be that the landlord of an estate is better placed to undertake such a project where it is of significant scale and with the long term commitment of an RHI scheme. However, smaller schemes may be suitable for tenants, more especially where they have medium or longer term security, but that raises a number of particular issues that will need to be addressed. These may often include:
- ensuring the handing of the contract to a subsequent occupier
- rent review issues
- compensation issues.

17.1.2   In many ways, an easy approach to the law and practice here is to think of the situation over the installation of an Aga or a central heating system. Who would do it and on what terms?

17.1.3   The parties will have to consider how the RHI payments are to be treated at the end of the lease and may wish to include in any consent agreement a requirement that the tenant will make arrangements to transfer the benefit of any remaining RHI payments to the landlord or an incoming tenant at the end of the term. Similar consideration may need to be given to any Green Deal commitment.

17.2   Fixtures and Chattels

17.2.1   A renewable heating system installed by a tenant could, either in whole or part, be either a chattel or a fixture, depending on the nature of the items installed. There is much case law on the subject (see most recently the House of Lords decision in *Elitestone v Morris* and the decision in *Botham v TSB*), but essentially a chattel has its own identity and is not a natural part of the property, whereas a fixture is an item attached to the land to make an improvement to the property. The prime tests to identify a fixture are the degree of the item's annexation to the land and the purpose for that annexation – if found to be a fixture it then passes with the property on its sale, lease or end of lease. The tenant's property in the item has ceased. Confusion can arise over this issue with regard to farms as agricultural holdings law (the 1986 and 1995 Acts and the Scottish 1991 Act) intervenes to give the tenant the statutory right to remove qualifying buildings and fixtures after they have been offered to the landlord (who has not then taken them) and other conditions have been met. The essential point is that, but for this statutory provision (and the common law treatment of trade and domestic ornamental fixtures), a fixture has become part of the landlord's property.

17.2.2   At this relatively early stage in the use of renewable heat technology, it seems likely that many items, such as biomass boilers and ground source heat pumps, would be regarded as 'fixtures'. It may be possible that others (solar collectors, for example) might be regarded as chattels if they could be removed from the property without causing damage. Case law may provide guidance in future. In general, the equipment will have most value in situ. If the tenant removes it, it may not then be certifiable for payments in any other location and there may be complications for the RHI agreement.

17.2.3   Where the work is carried out by the tenant, the value of that improvement or fixture should be disregarded at rent reviews. The Agricultural Holdings Acts allow the fixture to be considered if it was installed under an obligation of the tenancy.

17.3 Residential property

17.3.1 While most residential tenants are unlikely to wish to make the scale of investment necessary to install a renewable heating system into a rented property, those on longer leases or "improvement" leases might do so. The Green Deal may assist smaller schemes.

17.3.2 There is no statutory right to compensation for residential tenants, so the landlord's permission should be sought and terms for end of tenancy compensation agreed as part of the formal landlord's consent. The landlord's consent may not be unreasonably withheld under s.19(2) of the Landlord and Tenant Act 1927.

17.3.3 Where a landlord supplies heat to the property and seeks to recover the costs under a service charge, the tenant is protected against unreasonable charges by ss18 – 30 of the Landlord and Tenant Act 1985. This states that service charges must be reasonably incurred and the service supplied must be of a reasonable standard. Disputes can be referred to the Leasehold Valuation Tribunal.

17.4 Commercial property

17.4.1 A tenant of commercial property with a long enough lease might wish to install a renewable heating system into a let property on financial or ethical grounds, or to help the business in terms of corporate social responsibility targets or meeting environmental performance standards set by customers.

17.4.2 The Landlord and Tenant Act 1927 sets out the statutory rules for dealing with tenant's improvements in commercial property in England and Wales. Scottish commercial tenants essentially have freedom of contract and therefore the terms of the tenancy agreement and any subsequent agreement between the parties for the work will dictate how tenants' investments are treated.

17.4.3 The 1927 Act gives a tenant the right to claim compensation for improvements carried out during the tenancy, provided that the improvement meets certain criteria and that the correct procedures are followed throughout. This means that many tenants are not able to obtain compensation. Many landlords may have taken specific steps to exclude compensation. In such cases, the tenant will need to consider whether he will see an economic return on his investment in the remaining secure period of his tenancy. That will clearly be easier in longer tenancies, especially where the tenancy covers the whole period of the RHI commitment.

17.4.4 Section 1 of the Act states that the improvement:
- Must have been made by the tenant or his predecessor in title;
- Must not be a trade or other fixture which the tenant is entitled to remove;
- Must add to the letting value of the holding;
- Must not be an improvement made in fulfilment of a statutory or contractual obligation;
- Must have been made more than 3 years before the termination of the tenancy.

In the case of the installation of renewable heating systems, there may be cases where the landlord can argue that the works do not "add to the letting value of the holding".

17.4.5 The correct procedure for notifying the landlord in advance is quite long drawn out, but it *must* have been followed throughout for the improvement to be eligible for compensation at the end of the tenancy:

a) The tenant must serve notice of his intention to make the improvement on the landlord and any superior landlords, together with a plan and specification showing details of the improvement.

b) The landlord (and any superior landlord) has up to three months to respond. If no objection to the tenant's notice is served within three months then the tenant may proceed with the improvement and compensation will be due at the end of the tenancy.

c) If the landlord objects to the proposal, the tenant may apply to the court for a certificate confirming that the improvement is one which is eligible for compensation. All superior landlords should be included in any court action. The court will give a certificate confirming that the improvement is a "proper improvement" if it is satisfied that:
   i) The improvement is calculated to add to the letting value of the holding;
   ii) The improvement is reasonable and suitable to the character of the holding;
   iii) The improvement will not diminish the value of any other property belonging to the landlord or any superior landlord.
   The court may impose modifications to or conditions on the tenant's improvement proposal, including imposing a timescale for completion of the improvements. The landlord can offer to undertake the improvement works himself in return for a reasonable increase in rent. If such a proposal is accepted by the court, a timescale may be imposed and no certificate will be issued to the tenant unless the landlord fails to complete the works.

17.4.6 Where relevant, the amount of compensation which the landlord is obliged to pay for a tenant's improvements is limited by s.1 of the 1927 Act so that it "shall not exceed":

a) *the net addition to the value of the holding as a whole which may be determined to be the direct result of the improvement; or*
b) *the reasonable cost of carrying out the improvement at the termination of the tenancy, subject to a deduction of an amount equal to the cost (if any) of putting the works constituting the improvement into a reasonable state of repair, except so far as such cost is covered by the liability of the tenant under any covenant or agreement as to the repair of the premises.*

17.4.7 While the ceiling for the compensation is the "net addition to the value of the holding", s.1(2) of the 1927 Act unusually and specifically requires that the parties must consider the "purposes for which it is intended that the premises shall be used after the termination of the tenancy". If the landlord can demonstrate that the premises are to be demolished or substantially re-developed, for example, it may be that the improvement adds no net value. If the parties fail to agree the amount of compensation, s.1(3) allows the matter to be referred to the courts.

17.4.8 Contracting out – While it is not possible for a landlord to contract out of the provisions of Part 1 of the 1927 Act, action can be taken which will limit or avoid them. Most commonly used are:
- A requirement in the lease that the tenant reinstate the property at the end of the tenancy;
- A covenant in the lease obliging the tenant to carry out any improvement to which the landlord agrees;
- A decision by the landlord to demolish or re-develop the premises at the end of the lease.

17.5 Agricultural Tenancies

17.5.1 A renewable heat installation might be effected as landlord's improvement, a tenant's improvement or a tenant's fixture. As its operation and benefit will generally depend on the tenant, installing a farm level project as a landlord's improvement will require discussion and mutual agreement. If the tenant does it, he will usually want assurances as to the treatment of the facility when the tenancy ends. Much of the investment will usually, in land law terms, be a fixture and may, in practice, best be treated between the parties as a compensatable improvement rather than a fixture whose fate is left to the end of the tenancy.

17.5.2 Aside from any practical or economic grounds, the terms of any written tenancy may require the tenant to obtain landlord's consent before it he can sensibly proceed with a scheme, especially any major one.

17.6 Tenancies under the Agricultural Holdings Act 1986

17.6.1 **Tenant's improvements** – Improvements made by agricultural tenants in England and Wales with a tenancy under the Agricultural Holdings Act 1986 are eligible for compensation at the end of the term under s.64(1), if that improvement falls within Schedule 7 of the Act. However, this list is not well drafted in terms of renewable heat facilities. They may be covered by the "erection, alteration or enlargement of buildings..." (Schedule 7, Part II, Item 9) – a matter that is often regulated by the terms of written tenancy agreements. A more detailed discussion of tenant's improvements can be found in CAAV Numbered Publication 182 – End of Tenancy Compensation Under the Agricultural Holdings Act 1986. It is, of course, open to the parties to agree that a facility be treated on an improvements basis simply as a matter of contract between them.

17.6.2 Written consent for an improvement is a pre-requisite for any claim for compensation by the tenant and it should ideally be recorded in a memorandum of agreement which is then attached to the tenancy agreement. However, it does not have to be recorded in any particular format and written consent may, on occasion, be construed from other documents, such as the lease itself, a counter-signed grant application or even minuted notes of a meeting. Section 67(2) states that the consent may be conditional and conditions can relate to the amount of compensation.

17.6.3 If the landlord refuses to give consent for an improvement on the list within Part II of Schedule 7, the tenant may apply to the Agricultural Land Tribunal (ALT) for consent. The ALT may withhold or grant consent, or grant it subject to conditions, including conditions relating to compensation. If the ALT grants consent, the landlord can serve notice within one month proposing to carry out the work himself. If he does so, the tenant can be charged rent on the improvement.

17.6.4 In the absence of agreement between the parties, the assessment of the amount of compensation is addressed in s.66(1):

> "*The amount of any compensation under this Act for a relevant improvement specified in Schedule 7 to this Act shall be an amount equal to the increase attributable to the improvement in the value of the agricultural holding as a holding, having regard to the character and situation of the holding and the average requirements of tenants reasonably skilled in husbandry.*"

17.6.5 A common method of assessing the compensation due under s.66(1) is to take the increased rental value of the holding resulting from the improvement and multiply it by an appropriate number of years' purchase. The choice of the years' purchase figure will turn on the useful economic life of the improvement and the return on equivalent assets. There is no equivalent to s.1(2) of the Landlord and Tenant Act 1927, so the probable use of the holding after the end of the tenancy is not relevant.

17.6.6   However, the amount of compensation can also be agreed between the parties as part of the landlord's consent (s.67(2)). Traditionally this has often been addressed by writing-off the improvement over an agreed number of years to a nominal sum.

17.6.7   The landlord's consent should make provision for the outgoing tenant to co-operate over administrative issues at the end of the tenancy, including notifying the RHI administrators of the change in "owner" of the installation and arranging to transfer any outstanding RHI payments to the landlord or an incoming tenant.

17.6.8   **Tenant's Fixtures** – Where a fixture is not a compensatable improvement, it will be regarded as a "tenant's fixture". Under s.10 of the 1986 Act, the tenant has a defined power to remove qualifying fixtures (and "any engines"), provided that he has served at least one month's written notice on the landlord of his intention to remove the fixture. The landlord can then elect to purchase the fixture by serving a counter-notice under which he would retain the fixture, paying the tenant for it on the basis of its "fair value to an incoming tenant".

17.7   Farm Business Tenancies under the Agricultural Tenancies Act 1995
17.7.1   A more detailed consideration of compensation for end of tenancy matters under the Agricultural Tenancies Act is found in CAAV Numbered Publication 166A – Commentary on the Valuation of Improvements under the Agricultural Tenancies Act 1995.

17.7.2   Tenants with a Farm Business Tenancy (FBT) are entitled to compensation for improvements under s.16. The definition of an 'improvement' in s.15 includes:
> *"any physical improvement which is made on the holding by the tenant by his own effort or wholly or partly at his own expense..."*
This is a general definition with no list of specific qualifying items like that under the 1986 Act.

17.7.3   To be eligible for compensation, the tenant must have obtained the landlord's written consent (s.17) which may be conditional. If the landlord refuses to give consent, or if the conditions are unacceptable to the tenant, the tenant may refer the matter to arbitration (s.19) before undertaking the work.

17.7.4   The basis for the valuation of improvements is set out in s.20(1) of the Agricultural Tenancies Act:
> *"... the amount of compensation payable to the tenant under s16 of this Act in respect of any tenant's improvement shall be an amount equal to the increase attributable to the improvement in the value of the holding at the termination of the tenancy as land comprised in a tenancy."*
Again, there is no equivalent to s.1(2) of the Landlord and Tenant Act 1927 so the probable use of the holding after the end of the tenancy is not relevant.

17.7.5   The 2006 TRIG reforms introduced an alternative basis whereby the parties may agree on a ceiling for the compensation by inserting a new section 20(4A) which allows the parties to agree in writing that the compensation for an improvement will be the lesser of

- that calculated on the statutory basis under s.20(1); and
- the 'compensation limit'

The 'compensation limit' should be agreed between the parties in writing and may be a nominal sum, although case law suggests that it should not be nil. If the parties are unable to agree an amount, the limit will be "an amount equal to the cost to the tenant of making the improvement" (s.20(4B)). This provision offers a potential reassurance to landlords for whom the default basis might otherwise be an unquantifiable liability.

17.7.6 Tenant's Fixtures – Section 8 of the 1995 Act gives the tenant powers to remove qualifying fixtures and buildings provided he makes good any damage. There is no equivalent to the 1986 Act's procedure for the fixture to be offered to the landlord, but that may usually be the most sensible thing for a tenant to do where a renewable facility or part of one qualifies as a fixture rather than an improvement. Where this happens, it is then for the parties to agree as to any payment.

17.8   Tenancies under the Agricultural Holdings (Scotland) Acts 1991 and 2003
17.8.1 Tenant's Improvements – The Agricultural Holdings (Scotland) Act 1991 defines those items of fixed equipment provided by the tenant for which he can claim compensation. For fixed equipment to qualify for compensation on the end of the tenancy:
- It must be within the items listed in the Act's Schedule 5. Items potentially relevant to renewable energy include, according to the technology used:
  ○ 10 – construction of silos
  ○ 11 – making or improvement of farm access roads or service roads, bridges and fords (perhaps particularly relevant to wind turbines).
  ○ 12 – making or improvement of water courses, ponds or wells, or of works for the application of water power for agricultural or domestic purposes or for the supply of water for such purposes
  ○ 17 – provision or laying on of electric light or power including the provision of generating plant, fixed motors, wiring systems, switches and plug sockets
  ○ 18 – erection, alteration, or enlargement of buildings
  ○ 20 – the provision of barn machinery.
- The tenant must have followed the procedure required by the Act. For the items noted here, he must have given the appropriate proper notice to the landlord detailing the improvement and the manner in which the tenant proposes to carry it out. The landlord has one month from receipt of the notice to object to the improvement or the way in which it is to be carried out. The tenant can refer that objection to the Scottish Land Court.

17.8.2   Under s.36(1) of the Act, "the amount of any compensation payable to a tenant under this Part of this Act shall be such sum as fairly represents the value of the improvement to an incoming tenant", having taken account of any benefit that the landlord has given or allowed to the tenant in consideration the tenant carrying out the improvement (s.36(2)). Where both parties have funded the improvement, then any grant payment, subject to its conditions, is to be taken into account in the same proportion as the tenant's contribution to the improvement – that may be relevant to Renewable Heat Premium payments.

17.8.3   Section 45 of the Agricultural Holdings (Scotland) Act 2003 generally applies these provisions to Short Limited Duration Tenancies (SLDTs) and Limited Duration Tenancies (LDTs).

17.8.4 Tenant's Fixtures – Where an item of fixed equipment provided by the tenant is not a compensatable improvement, s.18(1) of the 1991 Act gives the tenant a conditional power to remove it. This applies to "any engine, machinery ... or other fixture" affixed the holding by the tenant and to any building erected by him unless it replaced an item of landlord's fixed equipment or was made under an obligation. The tenant, having paid all rent due and satisfied all other obligations to the landlord, must serve notice in writing of his intention to remove the item to the landlord at least a month before the end of the tenancy and the exercising of the right, whichever is the earlier. The landlord can then, before the tenant's notice expires, serve counter-notice electing to purchase the fixture or building but then pay a sum equal to the item's fair value to an incoming tenant. If the tenant does any avoidable damage to any other building or other part of the holding during the removal of the building or fixture, he shall make good all damage so occasioned, immediately after the removal (s.18(4)).

17.8.5 The 2003 Act makes no equivalent provision for tenants of SLDTs or LDTs who must therefore be careful to cover their position with regard to any substantial items of fixed equipment they may provide by contract if it cannot be a compensatable improvement.

17.8.6 Valuation – The statutory basis of valuation in Scotland for both tenant's fixtures and tenant's improvements is essentially the value to a hypothetical incoming tenant. That might raise issues where the item under consideration requires a degree of specialist expertise to manage as perhaps, for example, a bio-digester.

17.9 User Clauses

17.9.1 Written tenancy agreements conventionally contain clauses governing the use of the holding. In their most common forms, they limit the use to agricultural purposes but some are more limited still (as to dairying) or expressly allow approved diversification.

17.9.2 The force of an agriculture only user clause was considered by the Court of Appeal in *Jewell v McGowan* [2002] EWCA Civ 145. The tenancy agreement limited the use of the holding to "agricultural purposes only" and then excluded market garden uses. The tenant was operating an "open farm" on neighbouring land and proposed to use part of the let land for visitor parking, a trail and access connected with that open farm. The word "only" was found to exclude those uses, though not any uses such as walking that were de minimis. A more detailed consideration of *Jewell v McGowan* can be found in Appendix VII.

17.9.3 The nature of renewable heat may only rarely test this issue save where the heat would be exported from the agricultural business. Provided the heat is used for agricultural purposes (including dwellings used in the farm business), there should be no issue. The question might arise where the export of gas from an AD plant becomes a substantial activity. It will be more common for those renewable electricity projects which are mainly designed for export rather than use in the farm business.

17.9.4 Scotland – The 2003 Act gave Scottish tenants (except those with SLDTs) a greater ability to diversify, irrespective of the terms of a lease prohibiting non-agricultural use (s.39(2)). Its formal and detailed procedure is set out in s.40, and begins with the tenant giving 70 days prior written notice to the landlord specifying what the diversification is, where it is to be located, any changes to the land, when the diversification will start, and must address such matters on which the landlord could object (set out in s.40(9)(a)(i) to (ii)). There is then a timetable for the landlord to seek further information and then, if he wishes, to object. His silence will be deemed assent, save where the proposal is for the planting and cropping of trees (s.40(13)). The tenant can refer an objection to the Scottish Land Court for a decision.

17.9.5   Timber management may be relevant to biomass heat generation and so this procedure will apply where it is a non-agricultural use. The 2003 Act's s.42(1) gives the tenant of a 1991 Act tenancy or an LDT the right to cut timber from any trees planted by him after 27th November 2003, unless a provision in the lease limits this and provides for either compensation or a rent reduction.

17.9.6   Section 51(1) of the 2003 Act added a new s.45A of the 1991 Act to provide a framework for compensation and dilapidations, as appropriate, to be claimable in respect of a diversified use permitted under this procedure. The waygoing tenant can claim compensation equal to the fair value of the diversification activity to an incoming tenant of the holding on the usual rules for tenant's fixtures or improvements. This is excluded if the land is made unsuitable for agricultural use by an incoming tenant as a result of the diversification. A counter-claim for dilapidations is possible where the activity has reduced the value of the holding, or where dilapidation, deterioration or damage has been caused to any part of the holding or to anything in or on the holding.

17.9.7   Section 45A of the 1991 Act makes particular provisions for compensation between the parties where the tenant has planted trees for future cropping. It is assessed as the net difference between:
   – the trees, valued on the basis of their worth to a willing purchaser for future cropping, and
   – any loss of rent due to the landlord incurred by retaining the trees until the date of their cropping added to the cost of returning the land to agricultural use after cropping.

17.10   Heat supply agreements
17.10.1 In cases where the landlord chooses to install a system which will supply heat to let properties, the decision must be taken as to whether the supply of heat is included with the building in an all-inclusive rent, or whether it is billed separately. While an all-inclusive rent may appear more straightforward, VAT will have to be accounted for and there is no incentive for the tenant to minimise the heat consumed. If the supply of heat is to be invoiced separately, a heat meter should be installed so that readings can be taken to ensure accurate bills. With a ground source heat pump, it may only be necessary to charge for the electricity used by the pumps themselves.

17.10.2 A heat supply agreement might include the following terms:
   • The responsibilities of the parties
   • An undertaking to supply a specified amount of heat
   • The basis of how the charges are calculated – this may be by reference to an index of alternative fuel costs, or on a cost sharing basis, for example
   • How and when the charges will be reviewed
   • Apportionment of charges at the end of the term
   • Provision for disputes resolution
   • Contingency plans in the event of a failure of the system, which might include provision of back-up boilers or temporary heating.

SECTION E – UPDATE ON RENEWABLE ELECTRICITY

18. UPDATE ON RENEWABLE ELECTRICITY

18.1 Introduction

18.1.1 Having published The On-Farm Generation of Renewable Electricity in March 2011, this section offers a brief update on developments on that subject since then.

18.1.2 Major changes have been made to the Feed-in Tariff rates for solar photovoltaic schemes, with sharp reductions applying to schemes at more than domestic level that connect to the grid from 1st August 2011. The same review applied slight increases to anaerobic digestion schemes. The Budget announced changes to capital allowances and renewable projects have been denied access to the Enterprise Investment Scheme.

18.2 The Fast-Track Review of Feed-in Tariffs

18.2.1 The Department of Energy and Climate Change (DECC) published the results of its fast track review of Feed-in Tariffs (FiTs) (announced in March) for solar photovoltaic (pv) schemes and anaerobic digestion units in June 2011. With a wave of interest in solar farm schemes, DECC (like many governments on the continent) had become concerned at the poor value for money these would offer in expanding renewable electricity generation and so moved to cut back the FiT rates for schemes at more than domestic scale. It has increased the rates for new AD schemes.

18.2.2 The new rates, which will apply to any scheme, whenever work on it started, which is accredited for FiTs and commissioned from 1st August onwards, are as follows:

Solar pv rates:

Scale	New rate from 1/8/11
>50kW – 150kW	19.0p/kWh
>150kW – 250kW	15.0p/kWh
>250kW – 5MW and stand alone installations	8.5p/kWh

18.2.3 Rates for solar pv schemes of less than 50kW are unchanged from the original table produced in April 2010, which can be found in CAAV Numbered Publication 203 – The On-Farm Generation of Renewable Electricity.

AD rates:

Scale	New rate from 1/8/11
<250kW	14.0p/kWh
>250kw – 500kW	13.0p/kWh

18.2.4 The new rates will not be applied retrospectively, so that schemes which are accredited for FiTs and are commissioned before 1st August 2011 will be paid on the old rate. However, there will be no transitional arrangements for those who have already invested in schemes which will not be commissioned before 1st August.

18.2.5 The changes were made by amending the FiT payment rate table in the Standard Conditions of Electricity Supply Licences. The changes took effect from 1st August 2011.

18.2.6 The effect of the revised rates is that solar pv schemes of greater than 50kW are now very much less attractive to developers as they do not offer a high enough rate of return. Only a few large scale solar farms were able to obtain planning consent and complete construction and commissioning by 1st August. However, rooftop schemes can still offer good returns in the right locations.

18.2.7   The Department of Energy and Climate Change issued a further consultation in August 2011 on closing a potential loophole which could have allowed solar pv installations to add extensions to their sites at the pre-August 2011 Feed-in Tariff rates. There is sufficient ambiguity in the wording of the provision relating to extensions within 12 months of commissioning to suggest that some large scale solar developers might seek to use it to extend the size of their installations and claim the FiT rate applicable before August 2011. DECC considers that this is contrary to policy and proposes a "pre-emptive strike" to clarify the wording of the regulations so that the old FiT rate will not be available for extensions.

18.3   The Comprehensive Review of Feed-in Tariffs

18.3.1   DECC proposes to launch a full comprehensive review of Feed-in Tariffs later in 2011, which will report back by the end of the year. Any changes arising from that consultation will take effect from April 2012 – unless the review demonstrates an urgent need for changes before then. Assurances have been given that changes will not be retrospective.

18.3.2   The Comprehensive Review will consider tariff levels, degression rates, eligible technologies and interaction with other policies. In relation to wind power, it is expected to consider whether FiTs can be targeted to those wind farm developments which are situated in the best locations for harvesting wind energy.

18.4   UK Renewable Energy Roadmap

18.4.1   In July 2011 DECC published the UK Renewable Energy Roadmap, which is intended to set out a path to achieve the policy targets to deliver 15% of energy from renewable sources by 2010. The Roadmap identifies eight technologies which should help the Government to achieve this: onshore wind; offshore wind; marine energy; biomass electricity; biomass heat; ground and air source heat pumps and renewable transport.

18.4.2   For onshore wind, the Roadmap identifies that the risks to reaching its target include:

• Investor confidence – to be tackled by carefully planning the transition from Renewables Obligation to Feed-in Tariffs and implementing reforms to the electricity market;
• Planning permission – a combination of improved planning guidance and reforms to the planning system in England under the Localism Bill are proposed to reduce difficulties;
• Radar interference – a proposal to fund research and development into ways to reduce or mitigate interference with radar systems by wind turbines;
• Grid connection – work with Ofgem and National Grid to improve the process for securing new grid connections.

18.4.3   Biomass electricity includes electricity generated from landfill gas, co-fired power stations and anaerobic digesters as well as dedicated solid biomass systems, which may be either combined heat and power units or solely electricity generators. The 'priority actions' identified in the Roadmap for this sector are:

- Minimise investment risk – carefully plan the transition from Renewable Obligation to Feed-in Tariffs and implement reforms to the electricity market publish a Bioenergy Strategy later in 2011.
- Ensure a sustainable feedstock supply chain – link incentive payments to feedstock sustainability from 2013; publish a Greenhouse Gas Lifecycle Assessment Tool.
- Planning permission and consents – planning reform; work with agencies to ensure that policy approaches do not clash with existing environmental legislation.
- Long-term waste fuel contracts – expand supply chains for waste wood and solid recovered fuel; consider restrictions on sending waste wood to landfill
- Finance – provide support for innovation and demonstration projects.

18.5   Solar Panels – Installation as Breach of Covenants?

18.5.1   The Leasehold Valuation Tribunal has heard what might be the first case concerning rights to erect solar panels on the roof of a building – *Redmile v Butt and Shillingford* [2011]. A more detailed review of the case is set out in Appendix VIII.

18.5.2   Mr and Mrs Butt and Mr Shillingford installed solar panels on the roofs of houses they held on long leases from Redmile, who later applied to the Leasehold Valuation Tribunal for a direction that the erection of the solar panels on the two properties was in breach of a number of covenants attached to them, including:
- Not to make any alteration or addition to any building without Redmile's written consent, such consent not to be unreasonably withheld;
- Not to suffer anything which might be a nuisance or annoyance;
- Not to use the premises for any trade or business purpose.

18.5.3   The Tribunal held that the installation of the solar panels was an "addition" to the building which required Redmile's consent. Redmile were deemed to have refused consent and this was found to be unreasonable. Also, Redmile had accepted ground rent from the Butts after the solar panels were installed, thus they had waived the breach. No ground rent had been accepted from Mr Shillingford. Finally, the Tribunal concluded that there was no nuisance or annoyance, as there was no evidence that a reasonable person would find the panels any more annoying than the satellite dishes which were already common on the development.

18.6   Hydropower – The Environment Agency has streamlined its processes in dealing with hydropower applications to provide a better supported process for applicants. The Agency is consulting on proposed revisions to its Hydropower Good Practice Guidelines during summer 2011.

18.7   Microgeneration Strategy – On 22nd June 2011 the Department of Energy and Climate Change published a Microgeneration Strategy which considers the barriers (other than finance) to a wider uptake of microgeneration technology by consumers and community groups. It considers such issues as warranties and insurance, skills and training and consumer protection. The Strategy was developed in association with an industry group – the Microgeneration Government Industry Contact Group (GICG).

18.8   Anaerobic Digestion Strategy and Action Plan – In June 2011 the Department of Energy and Climate Change and the Department for the Environment, Food and Rural Affairs produced the Anaerobic Digestion Strategy and Action Plan in association with

industry representatives. The Action Plan advocates better communication and advice on AD, particularly for smaller potential users. Its recommendations include:

- further development of the online AD portal as a source of advice and guidance
- produce information on health and safety regulations for AD plants and advice on training
- collate and publish data on digestate use and on novel digestate products and markets
- hold a workshop on purpose-grown crops as AD feedstock
- better liaison with the financial sector to encourage investment and lending.

The AD Strategy and Action Plan can be found on the DEFRA website.

18.9   Wind Turbines – Natural England Guidance on Bats – Natural England has published an Interim Technical Information Note (TIN059) on the impact of single large wind turbines on bats. It considers both local bat populations and migratory patterns and proposes that bat surveys should be carried out between May and September where there is a risk that a proposed turbine might adversely affect bats. The Note, aimed at developers, planners and operators, can be downloaded from the Natural England website.

18.10   Anaerobic Digester Pollution Incident – In an unreported case cited by the Environment Agency, a company behind an anaerobic digestion plant in Norfolk was prosecuted for causing pollution to a watercourse and fined a total of £5,000 plus costs. The AD plant was to process waste vegetables from the food-processing industry, but a backlog of material built up in inadequate storage facilities when the company had problems getting the digester to work properly. Liquid from the rotting vegetables escaped into field drains and ended up in a local watercourse. The Environment Agency said that the case highlighted the importance of planning ahead and testing drainage systems thoroughly before use.

18.11   Enterprise Investment Scheme and Renewables – The 2011 Budget included proposals that companies whose trade consists wholly or substantially of the receipt of Feed-in Tariffs or similar subsidies will only be eligible for the EIS where commercial electricity generation starts by 6 April 2012. Shares issued before 23rd March 2011 will not be affected. Legislation is expected to be introduced in the Finance Bill 2012.

18.12   Capital Allowances – The Government is considering a proposal to withdraw the opportunity to claim capital allowances for plant and machinery which is used to claim Feed-in Tariffs or Renewable Heat Incentive payments. A consultation took place in summer 2011 and draft legislation is expected in the autumn, with any changes likely to take effect from April 2012. Further detail can be found at 14.1 above.

18.13   Scottish Agri-Renewables Strategy – in August 2011, Scottish Minister Richard Lochhead announced that a Scottish Agri-Renewables Strategy was to be developed to guide and support this emerging industry.

APPENDIX I – LEGISLATION AND CASE LAW

LEGISLATION
EU Directives
Energy Performance of Buildings Directive 2010/31/EU
Measuring Instruments Directive 2004/22/EC
Renewable Energy Directive 2009/28/EC
Waste Incineration Directive 2000/76/EC

UK Acts of Parliament
Agricultural Holdings Act 1986
Agricultural Holdings (Scotland) Act 1991
Agricultural Holdings (Scotland) Act 2003
Agricultural Tenancies Act 1995
Clean Air Act 2003
Climate Change (Scotland) Act 2009
Energy Act 2008
Landlord and Tenant Act 1927
Landlord and Tenant Act 1985

Statutory Instruments
SI 991/2007   The Energy Performance of Buildings (Certificates and Inspections) (England and Wales) Regulations
SI 2363/2008 The Energy Performance of Buildings (Certificates and Inspections) (England and Wales) Regulations
SSI 309/2008 The Energy Performance of Buildings (Scotland) Regulations
SSI 136/2011 The Town and Country Planning (General Permitted Development) (Non-Domestic Microgeneration) (Scotland) Amendment Order
The Renewable Heat Regulations 2011 *(SI number unknown at time of going to press)*

CASE LAW
Botham v TSB Bank plc [1996] EWCA Civ 778
Elitestone Ltd v Morris [1997] UKHL 15
Honiton & District Agricultural Association v Wonnacott [1955] 48 Rating and Income Tax Cases 589
Jewell v McGowan [2002] EWCA Civ 145
Redmile v Butt and Shillingford [2011] LVT MAN/00CF/LBC/2011/0002 and 0003

APPENDIX II – OTHER SOURCES OF ADVICE

Anaerobic Digestion and Biogas Association www.adbiogas.co.uk
Carbon Trust www.carbontrust.co.uk
'Biomass Heating – a practical guide for potential users' (CTG012) can be downloaded
    from the Carbon Trust website
Combined Heat and Power Association www.chpa.co.uk
Committee on Climate Change www.theccc.org.uk
Energy Saving Trust www.energysavingtrust.org.uk
Energyshare www.energyshare.com
Enhanced Capital Allowances www.eca.gov.uk
Forestry Commission Biomass Energy Centre www.biomassenergycentre.org.uk
Ground Source Heat Pump Association www.gshp.org.uk
Heat Pump Association www.heatpumps.org.uk
Microgeneration Certification Scheme www.microgenerationcertification.org
Ofgem www.ofgem.gov.uk
Renewable Energy Association www.r-e-a.net
Scottish Woodfuel website www.usewoodfuel.co.uk
Welsh Woodfuel website www.woodfuelwales.org.uk

APPENDIX III – GLOSSARY OF TERMS

AD   Anaerobic digestion
CHP   Combined heat and power
DECC   Department of Energy and Climate Change
EA   Environment Agency
FiTs   Feed-in Tariffs
Ofgem   the Gas and Electricity Markets Authority
pv   Photovoltaic
RHI   Renewable Heat Incentive
RO   Renewables Obligation
SEPA   Scottish Environment Protection Agency

APPENDIX IV – "MAJOR RENOVATIONS" UNDER THE ENERGY PERFORMANCE OF BUILDINGS DIRECTIVE

Where a building has a 'major renovation', the Directive requires the member state to ensure that either the whole building or the renovated part meets current minimum energy performance requirements.

> "Member States shall take the necessary measures to ensure that when buildings undergo major renovation, the energy performance of the building or the renovated part thereof is upgraded in order to meet minimum energy performance requirements ..." Article 7

Major renovation is defined in Article 2(10) in two ways and it is for each member state to decide which interpretation they will choose:

a) the total cost of the renovation relating to the building envelope or the technical building systems is higher than 25% of the value of the building, excluding the value of the land upon which the building is situated; or

b) more than 25% of the surface of the building envelope undergoes renovation.

The actual operation of Article 7 will turn on how the UK implements this provision in its national legislation, but it is assumed that "renovation", being undefined in the Directive, has its usual meaning. In the OECD, "renovate" means to renew materially, to repair, to restore by replacing lost or damaged parts, or to create anew and "renovation" is construed accordingly. It may be a matter of interpretation in the light of the facts of any case whether an extension amounts to a renovation.

For option (a), the Directive does not specify the basis on which "value" is to be assessed – by default, it is assumed to be "market value" assessed in accordance with conventional valuation standards unless there is good reason to adopt another basis. It is a comparison of the cost of the proposed work with the value of the building, having excluded the value of the land under the building. The test does not ask for an apportionment of value but the exclusion of the value of the land. That option would mean that in most cases, this test appears to require two valuations for any building that would ordinarily be sold with its underlying land:

– one of the building as it would be sold with the land

– another of the underlying land without the building (likely to be with the benefit of any development value).

The resulting net figure is then to be compared with the cost of the proposed works. As cost is a different concept from value, especially for the adaptation of buildings, this test may often require the upgrading of the energy performance of the building where the value added by the work is less than 25% of the apportioned value of the building.

Option (b) appears to require an assessment of:

– the total external area of the building, including its walls and roofs, and

– how much of that area would be subject to the renovation.

This might mean that a purely internal renovation would not be caught by option (b) but be caught by option (a).

If the renovation proves to be "major" under the test adopted by the member state, then the Directive appears unclear whether it is the whole building or just the renovated part of it that is to be ungraded to minimum energy performance standards. That may be for the member state to say.

APPENDIX V – HEAT MEASUREMENT, SCALE AND CAPACITY

Heat is, strictly speaking, the term used to describe the energy within a system. It is measured in joules. Generally, the more thermal energy a system has, the higher its temperature will be. Measures of thermal energy include joules (J), kilogram calories (kcal), British Thermal Units (BTU), watts (W) and therms, to name a few of the most commonly used.

Definition of Units

Unit	Symbol	Definition
Joule	J	work (energy) required to produce 1 watt for 1 second.
Calorie	calorie	amount of energy required to raise the temperature of 1 gram of water by 1° Centigrade, (usually used in smaller scale experiments).
Kilogram calorie	Kcal	amount of energy required to raise the temperature of 1 kilogram of water by 1° Centigrade. This is the more widely used unit. It is the "calorie" that is used to describe the energy value of foods.
Watt	W	power required to produce 1 joule for 1 second. *Power* is the rate at which *energy* is consumed or generated.
Kilowatt thermal	KW_{th}	1000 (10^3) Watts of thermal power.
Megawatt thermal	MW_{th}	1,000,000 (10^6) Watts of thermal power.
British Thermal Unit	B.T.U.	amount of energy required to raise the temperature of 1 pound of water by 1° Fahrenheit.
Therm	thm	the energy equivalent to burning 10 cubic feet (1ccf) of natural gas (at standard temperature and pressure). Therm factor is used to convert a volume of gas to its heat equivalent to calculate energy use.
Therm*ie*	th	amount of energy required to raise the temperature of 1 tonne of water by 1° Centigrade.

The basic unit of measurement for thermal energy generation is the power taken over the time that it is taken: the kilowatt hour thermal (KWh_{th}). This is one kilowatt thermal operating for one hour.

APPENDIX VI – SCHEDULE 1 OF THE RENEWABLE HEAT INCENTIVE REGULATIONS: INFORMATION FOR ACCREDITATION

SCHEDULE 1   Regulations 22, 24, 25, 26 and 36
Information required for accreditation and registration

1.—(1) This Schedule specifies the information that may be required of a prospective participant in the scheme.

(2) The information is, as applicable to the prospective participant—

(a) name, home address, e-mail address and telephone number;

(b) any company registration number and registered office;

(c) any trading or other name by which the prospective participant is commonly known;

(d) details of a bank account in the prospective participant's name which accepts pound sterling deposits in the United Kingdom;

(e) information to enable the Authority to satisfy itself as to the identity of the individual completing the application;

(f) where an individual is making an application on behalf of a company, evidence which satisfies the Authority, that the individual has authority from the company to make the application on its behalf;

(g) details of the eligible installation owned by the prospective participant including its cost;

(h) evidence, which satisfies the Authority, as to the ownership of the eligible installation;

(i) evidence that the eligible installation was new at the time of installation;

(j) where an eligible installation has replaced a plant, details of the plant replaced;

(k) evidence which demonstrates to the Authority's satisfaction the installation capacity of the eligible installation;

(l) details of the fuel which the prospective participant is proposing to use;

(m) in relation to prospective participants generating heat from biomass, notification as to whether the prospective participant is proposing to use solid biomass contained in municipal waste and, if so, whether or not the prospective participant is regulated under the Environmental Permitting (England and Wales) Regulations 2010 or the Pollution Prevention and Control (Scotland) Regulations 2000;

(n) where the plant is a heat pump, evidence which demonstrates to the Authority's satisfaction, that the heat pump meets a coefficient of performance of at least 2.9;

(o) in respect of a producer of biogas or biomethane, details of the feedstock which the producer is proposing to use;

(p) details of what the heat generated will be used for and an estimate of how much heat will be used;

(q) details of the building in which the heat will be used;

(r) the industry sector for which the heat will be used;

(s) details of the size and annual turnover of the prospective participant's organisation;

(t) details of other plants generating heat which form part of the same heating system as the eligible installation to which the application relates;

(u) where regulation 13 applies, evidence from the installer that the requirements specified in that regulation are met;

(v) such information as the Authority may specify to enable it to satisfy itself that the requirements of Chapter 3 of Part 2 have been met including—

(i) evidence that a class 2 heat meter, other heat meter or steam measuring equipment has been installed;

(ii) evidence that the class 2 heat meter, other heat meter or steam measuring equipment was calibrated prior to use;

(iii) in relation to all heat meters, details of the meter's manufacturer, model, meter serial number;

(iv) a schematic diagram showing details of the heating system of which the eligible installation forms part, including all plants generating and supplying heat to that heating system, all purposes for which heat supplied by that heating system is used, the location of meters and associated components and such other details as may be specified by the Authority;

(v) where—

    (aa) an eligible installation has an installation capacity of $1MW_{th}$ or above, or

    (bb) regulation 17 applies, if so requested by the Authority, an independent report by a competent person verifying that such of those requirements as the Authority may specify have been met;

(w) such other information as the Authority may require to enable it to consider the prospective participant's application for accreditation or registration.

(3) Information specified in this Schedule must be provided in such manner and form as the Authority may reasonably request.

(4) The costs of providing the information specified in this Schedule are to be borne by the applicant.

APPENDIX VII – AGRICULTURAL USER CLAUSES: *JEWELL v MCGOWAN*

The force of an agriculture only user clause was considered by the Court of Appeal in *Jewell v McGowan* [2002] EWCA Civ 145. The tenancy agreement limited the use of the holding to "agricultural purposes only" and then excluded market garden uses. The tenant was operating an "open farm" on neighbouring land and proposed to use part of the let land for visitor parking, a trail and access connected with that open farm. The word "only" was found to exclude those uses, though not any uses such as walking that were de minimis.

Agriculture is generally but not exhaustively defined by s.96 of the 1986 Act (and by s.38(1) of the 1995 Act and s.85(1) of the Scottish 1991 Act):

> ""agriculture" includes horticulture, fruit growing, seed growing, dairy farming and livestock breeding and keeping, the use of land as grazing land, meadow land, osier land, market gardens and nursery grounds, and the use of land for woodlands where that use is ancillary to the farming of land for other agricultural purposes, and "agricultural" shall be construed accordingly."

While the subject tenancy would remain protected by the 1986 Act, the proposed uses were supplemental to its primary agricultural use. The Court of Appeal held that the word "only" had to be given its natural and effective meaning and did not allow such exceptions as might not substantially affect the character of the tenancy, however much that might lie within s.1(2) of the 1986 Act: "... the word was intended to prohibit all activities other than the use for agricultural purposes, except for activities which are de minimis."

However, the Court of Appeal then illustrated that this was not an absolute prohibition on any non-agricultural use and

> "does not mean that the requirement to use the holding "for agricultural purposes only" is to be read in any extreme or unreasonable sense. Where a dwelling house is part of an agricultural tenancy or permitted by a tenancy agreement, such a provision must necessarily allow it to be inhabited in the ordinary way. ... there are clearly other things which a farmer may still do on land which will fall to be regarded as peripheral or minimal, and do not mean that he is using the land for non-agricultural purposes. No-one would, for example, sensibly suggest that clause 22 would be infringed by a farmer or his family or friends walking picnicking, sketching or fishing on his land for pleasure."

The Court referred to the Lands Tribunal's decision in the rating case, *Honiton & District Agricultural Association v. Wonnacott* [1955] 48 Rating and Income Tax Cases 589. The statute in question said "Agricultural land" means any land used as arable or pasture land only ...". The Court cited the Tribunal's decision that "the use of a field for one day in a year (which did not in any way interfere with or interrupt the use of the lands as pasture or meadows, as the grass was removed before the show and the show took place during the normal rest period given to the land) was disregarded as de minimis." It then contrasted that with the case in hand where the use was so "extensive as to involve up to 10,000 visitors a year and to contribute up to one-third of the farm's income".

The question was whether the open farm activities proposed on the let land would lie within the definition of agriculture. Ancillary activities could have a different character and in this case while the open farm was founded on the life of a dairy farm, it was essentially educational. "It is a separate commercial activity, for purposes of profit, and its character or purpose cannot be derived from the fact that the respondent may choose to devote its profits to the farm.".

APPENDIX VIII – A REVIEW OF *REDMILE v BUTT AND SHILLINGFORD* [2011]

In *Redmile v Butt and Shillingford* [2011] MAN/OOCF/LBC/2011/0002 and 0003, the Leasehold Valuation Tribunal heard what is perhaps the first case concerning rights to erect solar panels on the roof of a building.

Mr and Mrs Butt and Mr Shillingford held long leases of detached houses in a development owned and built by Redmile. In spring 2010, the Butts entered an agreement with a solar panel provider whereby solar panels were installed on the house roof at nil cost. The terms of the arrangement were that the Butts were entitled to free electricity when the solar panels were generating and the installer kept the Feed-in Tariff payments plus income from any unused electricity which was exported to the national grid. Mr Shillingford entered into a similar arrangement with the same solar panel provider a few months later.

In January 2011, Redmile applied to the Leasehold Valuation Tribunal for a direction that the erection of the solar panels on the two properties was in breach of a number of covenants attached to them. Those covenants included the following:
- "Not to erect or make or permit or suffer to be erected or made any alteration in or addition to any building ..." without Redmile's written consent, such consent not to be unreasonably withheld;
- Not to suffer anything which might be a nuisance or annoyance;
- Not to use the premises for any trade or business purpose.

The Tribunal held that:
1. The installation of the solar panels was an "addition" to the building which required Redmile's consent. Redmile were deemed to have refused consent and this was found to be unreasonable in these circumstances, because the technical challenges (loading on the roof and invalidation of the NHBC warranty) were not sustained. The only other ground of objection was aesthetic impact and it would have been disproportionate to have upheld Redmile's objection on that alone.
2. Redmile had accepted ground rent from the Butts after the solar panels were installed, thus they had waived the breach. No ground rent had been accepted from Mr Shillingford.
3. The test for whether there was a nuisance and annoyance was held to be an objective one, based on whether a "reasonable person" would be "annoyed and aggrieved" (*Tod-Heatley v Banham* [1888]). There was no evidence that a reasonable person would find the panels any more annoying than the satellite dishes which were already common on the development.
4. There was no business use of the properties, or if there was, it was of a nature such that it was ancillary or subordinate to the domestic use.

Although this case concerned houses let on long leaseholds, some of the conclusions reached by the Tribunal might offer guidance in other circumstances. In particular, the Tribunal found that the panels were not dissimilar in impact from satellite dishes, of which there were already a number on properties in the development for which no permission had been sought from Redmile.

The issue of whether there is a business use is likely to hang on the particular facts of the case. If the occupier received an income directly arising from the solar panels, another tribunal or court might take a different view on whether that constituted a business use.